CREW RESOURCE MANAGEMENT

CREW RESOURCE MANAGEMENT

Awareness, Cockpit Efficiency & Safety

Captain Brian McAllister

AAIM, AAIEX, AMBIM, FAI DIP (1st) LON.

For General Aviation and Airline, Single-Crew and Multi-Crew Flight Operations

Airlife

England

First published in the UK in 1997
by Airlife Publishing Ltd

British Library Cataloguing-in Publication Data
A catalogue record for this book
is available from the British Library

ISBN 1 85310 903 7

Typeset by Servis Filmsetting Ltd, Manchester
Printed in England by Livesey Ltd, Shrewsbury

Airlife Publishing Ltd

101 Longden Road, Shrewsbury SY3 9EB, England.

This book is dedicated to my wife, Audrey, whose continued and unstinting support of my many literary activities can never be adequately repaid.

BY THE SAME AUTHOR

The Instrument Pilot – PPL & Beyond
Flying the Edge

CONTENTS

The Power of Thinking

Whatever withdraws us from the power of our senses; whatever makes the past, the distant, or the future predominate over the present; advances us in the dignity of thinking beings.

Samuel Johnson

Introduction

Accident investigation experience indicates that airline captains have often failed at critical moments in the flight to take advantage of important resources that are available to them. These resources have included not only available equipment and support services, but the assistance of the co-ordinated crew.

The human factor

In our quest for safety in aviation we focus attention on all the obvious deficiencies, like mechanical failures and bad errors of judgement in airmanship. It is my belief this approach is too simplistic. For example, why do experienced and well-trained pilots on occasion fly incorrect approach procedures, or run dangerously low on fuel? Any aviator knows this as the *human factor*, which plays a vital role in aviation safety.

A growing understanding of human interaction and behaviour is now developing fast to help find the answers to these questions. It also assists us in concentrating on ways to improve operational safety and efficiency. In fact, since the study of human factors (HF) in aviation came to the forefront, a great deal has been learned about how to manage and improve cockpit safety. This is mainly through a greater understanding of the way pilots behave individually and collectively, with and without the pressures of stress. Ignorance is certainly not bliss in any part of aviation, nor an excuse. Pilots in particular need to be regularly informed about human aspects of safety and how to manage them.

What we are really talking about here is Crew Resource Management (CRM), which is being increasingly recognised as an essential element in maintaining high cockpit safety standards. It is certainly complementary to Line Orientated Flight Training (LOFT). The training involves complete flightcrews using representative flights on a real-time basis, to practise normal, abnormal and emergency operations as a team. The basic reason for this training is not to test competence, but to allow flightcrews to develop and learn how to work together effectively in all situations.

The trouble is, many pilots do not know what CRM is, even though the concept was originally developed in the USA as far back as the early 1980s. When introduced to the subject, some *ab initio* students have stated, 'So you really mean Managing Cockpit Safety?' Partly correct, of course, except I point out that CRM is a far more complex subject than that; and it has no 'magic formula' solution. Now, the benefits of CRM are being fully appreciated and it is being given the prominence it deserves.

CRM was originally developed for two- or even three-crew airline operations. However, it needed some modification for General Aviation (GA) use. The terminology is still accurate though to describe CRM's training role for single-pilot operations.

CRM broadens pilots' knowledge

In relation to airlines, CRM has broadened its scope to include Crew/Company Resource Management. But whichever title it is given, for whatever operation, its primary purpose results in an improvement in flight safety through a better understanding and actual *management* of the human factor aspects of flight operations. For large airlines, CRM training might well take the form of a self-debrief following a filmed simulator exercise. The crew watch the video of themselves and discuss the result – good and bad – then devise ways on how to improve performance. Smaller GA operations, on the other hand, may view a video in which pilots re-enact the scenario prior to a real in-flight incident, or accident, and discuss in detail what led to the errors. For single-crew operation, cockpit efficiency and the quality of decision-making are examined.

The impact of JARs

European Joint Aviation Regulations (JARs) even include CRM training requirements for a pilot flying a light single-engine aircraft on commercial transport operations. Looking at the long term, how much benefit this will eventually produce in practice is a matter of conjecture. What I can say is that any training that improves flight safety is worthwhile.

CRM develops self-discipline

We can now see that CRM usage must be an 'interactive experience'. Therefore CRM training has to be *participative* in nature and have meaningful content. It does not consist of a rigid syllabus, and this is as it should be because there are so many variables.

Those who attend the seminar training sessions teach themselves with the help of an appropriately qualified facilitator – an instructor with the job of prompting discussion among the course participants. This will cover exercises in which they have taken part, but pilots draw up their own agenda for CRM training. Not only does the seminar help them appraise what they do, but the opportunity exists to discuss problems with more experienced pilots under the trainer's guidance. The result is an improved awareness, with the natural spin-off being an increase in self-discipline and efficiency in the cockpit. The beauty of the system is that it is able to provide help to all types of operation.

CRM training, therefore, deals with pilots who have widely differing backgrounds and experience, from low-time civil pilots to older military pilots with thousands of hours on fast jets. To my mind this merely confirms the importance of CRM training, because two pilots from different ends of the operational spectrum could well end up together on the same flight deck. CRM strengthens the essential link between academic concepts and practical application.

CRM provides a levelling factor

Within each group which attends CRM seminars there is a wide variety of abilities, technical knowledge, attitudes and understanding of what makes flying safe, plus the ability to cope with commercial pressures. CRM seminars provide the opportunity to 'level the CRM knowledge playing field'. Pilots soon realise that they face the same basic problems, from whatever part of the aviation (operational) spectrum they come. The best way of doing this is the use of video recording during training sessions. Playback and subsequent discussion among the individual groups provide for a stimulating exchange of views. With the variation of available equipment for trainers, creativity and innovation are vital to create the right atmosphere.

Showing the re-enactment of cockpit sequences leading to familiar accidents is definitely a powerful method in persuading pilots of their human fallibility. Regular training sessions which review scenarios of known emergencies and the methods of dealing with them enhance 'pattern recognition' in the area of CRM and Practical Cockpit Management. This is part of the 5A Pyramid Concept I've devised which is discussed later in this book, a concept that deals with the important inter-relationship of Aircrew, Aircraft Type, Equipment, Support Personnel and Airspace.

Like the strands of a spider's web, we will pull all the various aspects of CRM together piece by piece: HF, Practical Cockpit Management, Managing

Cockpit Safety, Human Stress Factors (HSF), Pilot Judgement and Decision-Making, plus the Cause and Circumstance of Accidents, and much more. This book will then provide a sound basis for a general study of CRM. It can be used before attending any formal seminars, or for consolidation of subject areas afterwards.

CHAPTER 1

ASSIMILATION OF KNOWLEDGE IN THE AUTOMATED TECHNOLOGICAL ENVIRONMENT

There is a marked difference between the information available to us and the knowledge we actually possess; technology gurus continually try to imply the exact opposite. If we look at it logically, information is merely raw data. By definition, knowledge implies a certain level of understanding, and this requires study and analysis over a period of time.

One of the major questions that 'trainers' of all aviation disciplines continually have to address concerns the limitations of *memory* and *attention span*. For aircrew, this is particularly important when under stress. We need to know how the human mind absorbs information in a variety of circumstances; also, how it adapts to data being presented by the latest automated computer technology, and in what way. All aircrew need to understand more about the decision-making process in general, and their own in particular. But can they cut through the array of information being presented using mental short-cuts, so they can quickly get to grips with what must be achieved? It is all about the vital importance of communication in the automated technological environment.

One of the main building blocks of knowledge is well-planned and consistent, recurrent training. This is the most efficient way to build up our 'knowledge experience', not only in aircraft systems but also in terms of the wider concept of better Crew Resource Management and the spin-off benefits that brings. Both are equally important in today's aviation. An understanding of human factors gives us a starting point, the basic key to the whole subject, but initial training is the introduction, the first transfer of information, and this should not be a burden either in time spent or amount of content. In this way information can mature into lasting and meaningful knowledge.

Requirement for general technological training

Investigation of some advanced technology incidents has found that some pilots have not had a complete understanding of all the automated

Advanced technology on the flight deck
(*Photo courtesy of Boeing*)

features available to them. Faced with very flexible automated systems with a range of modes, some pilots have relied on a limited variety of strategies to operate the aircraft. In unusual situations, however, pilots may be required to have a thorough understanding of obscure or little-used aspects of the automation. That is, according to one leading aircraft manufacturer; and there is no reason to doubt that statement as evidence points in that direction.

Conversion training to advanced technology aircraft involves standard solutions to standard problems, as one senior check pilot put it. But a strictly rule-based approach to operating aircraft may not give sufficient emphasis to the need for pilots to have a good knowledge of aircraft systems. There may be a need to ensure that pilots have a deeper understanding of the systems they are operating, which really means the specific type aircraft they currently fly.

How organisational conditions introduce errors

It all reverts to *management attitudes*, because advanced automated systems enable new aircraft to be operated more economically than older-generation aircraft, and in the great majority of cases to carry more passengers as well. Nevertheless, many airline managements who are anxious to reduce costs seem to be encouraging crews to use automation in circumstances where the pilots would prefer to fly the aircraft manually. This has been referred to as the 'we bought it, you use it' management line of (policy) thinking.

Understanding the problems

The study and investigation-research into advanced technology flight deck accident and incident issues, as you can imagine, is quite involved and like a multi-headed Hydra. In many respects, the new types of error which occur in these aircraft are more like teething problems in an everyday computer system for a major company; they don't resemble traditional aviation problems.

To find solutions and overcome these errors, it is vital to deal with the conditions which promote them. One of the most important aspects is to keep pilots 'in the loop' (of the entire system), in other words to make sure they remain aware of the mode status of the aircraft they are flying at all times, and that they have a sound understanding of the 'system behaviour' of the aircraft. To make sure that crews have adequate mental models of automated systems, the training must emphasise not only rule-based learning, but additionally a detailed knowledge of the systems.

Systems awareness

A loss of systems awareness occurs when the pilot is unaware of the system state of the aircraft, or develops an erroneous idea of how the systems perform in particular situations. In some cases the pilot may be unaware of basic system capabilities or limitations.

In 1985 a Boeing B-747 flying at 41,000 ft over the Pacific suffered a loss of power on one of its four engines. The aircraft was not capable of maintaining that altitude on three engines. Unaware of this limitation, the crew took no action and when the authority of the autopilot to correct the yaw was exceeded, the aircraft rolled almost inverted and the nose dropped to a near-vertical attitude. The aircraft was recovered at 9,500 ft. The crew initially believed that the unusual attitude shown on their instruments was due to instrument failure.

Mode awareness

Automated systems can operate in a variety of modes. If the pilot thinks he has engaged one mode when actually another is activated, the results can be disastrous. A 1989 study (Wiener) of pilots flying the Boeing B-757 found that only about 70% of pilots always claimed to know the selected autopilot or flight director mode. When transitioning from one aircraft to another, some pilots have been confused about how to disengage modes, particularly when automatic mode changes occur.

During final descent, the pilots were unable to de-select the approach mode after localiser and glidepath capture when ATC suddenly requested that the aircraft maintain the current altitude and initiate a 90° turn for spacing. They tried to select the altitude hold and heading select modes in an attempt to disengage the approach mode. When this did not work they disconnected all autoflight systems (Sarter and Woods).

System 'workarounds'

There have been reports that airline crews have sometimes intentionally entered incorrect data into the Flight Management Computer (FMC), simply to achieve a specific desired result. It appears that such 'workarounds' are common in automated systems. This reflects a desire of crews to enact what has been described as 'smoothing out inelegant automation'.

Crews who wished to start a vertical navigation descent earlier than their computed top of descent (TOD) point discovered at least two ways to cause the FMC to recompute the TOD. One was to enter a point for use of thermal anti-ice on the descent page, even though there was no intention of using it. The other method was more precise, and involved simply entering a fictitious tailwind (Wiener). These methods would, of course, achieve the desired result, but would tend to defeat the purpose of the computer calculating fuel-efficient descent profiles. The problem then arises that any situation which involves the input of incorrect data into aircraft systems is definitely very undesirable. What it does show is the strong possibility of inadequate training or, worse still, system design.

Situational awareness also means system awareness

Loss of situational awareness occurs when the pilot develops an erroneous perception of the state of the aircraft in relation to the outside world. Following programming of a navigation computer, pilots should maintain an awareness of the aircraft position in relation to the flight-planned track, not merely letting the aircraft do all the work.

Awareness of operating modes requires frequent checking of system indicators, not only to make sure the correct mode is selected, but also to detect when a *system* or *mode* disconnects. To emphasise the point, let's look at two particular examples:

Shortly after the introduction of commercial jet transports, a Boeing B-707 flying at 35,000 ft experienced an autopilot disconnect and began a downward spiral. The crew did not detect the uncoupling of the autopilot until well after the initial loss of control. The crew finally recovered the aircraft at about 6,000 ft above the Atlantic.

While attempting to diagnose a landing gear unsafe light in a Lockheed L-1011, the crew failed to notice that the autopilot disconnected, probably because one of the crew members bumped the control wheel. The aircraft slowly descended from 2,000 ft and crashed.

Mode misapplication – failures or errors

Most automated aircraft systems usually have the option of being operated in a variety of modes. Confusion of operating mode, or perhaps the selection of the wrong mode, is sometimes the result of the many possibilities available to the pilot. This situation is at times compounded by inadequate or poorly directed training.

We must remember System Mode Status is an important element of a new-generation aircraft pilot's cockpit scan. Although this is displayed to the pilot, a 'mode status' may be easily missed or forgotten among the wealth of other CRT data on the flight deck. Let's illustrate this with another example:

The aircraft was climbing to FL410 with the autopilot and throttles engaged. At approximately FL350 the airspeed was observed to be below 180 kts and decaying. The autopilot was disengaged and the pitch attitude decreased. At this point the stick shaker activated and a small buffet was felt. Application of full power and a further decrease in pitch attitude returned the airspeed to normal (ICAO).

The pilot of this same aircraft later reported that he believed the autopilot was in the flight level change mode (maximum climb power and climbing while maintaining a selected airspeed or Mach). In retrospect, he felt that the autopilot must have been in vertical speed mode, 2,500 feet per minute. If this in fact was the case, then the airspeed would have remained close to normal until about FL300. At this point the airspeed would reduce as the autopilot attempted to maintain the vertical speed. In 1992, the Strasbourg crash of an Airbus A320 involved a mode misapplication. The crew believed the aircraft was descending in flight path angle mode, rather than vertical speed mode.

Monitoring failures

As the role of the pilot increasingly becomes that of a Systems Monitor, rather than a Direct System Controller, then monitoring failures can be expected to escalate. This will become a growing problem on the flight deck of advanced technology aircraft. A great deal of research has indicated that aircrew are not well suited simply for passive monitoring tasks. Therefore an individual crew member whose main task is to monitor various displays is very likely to suffer a reduction in performance as time passes. Nowhere is this more apparent than on long-haul flights, even with two crews. However, this subject is discussed in some detail later in the book.

Technological malfunction and human error

Whatever discussion there is about the new technology, there is no doubt it has benefited aviation generally. The application of modern computer processors to most aircraft systems means that many functions can be automated and integrated with other functions, so the massive volume of stored information on board the aircraft enables the aircraft to *know* where it is, and have detailed route data, radio and navigation aid frequencies. This allows the aircraft to manage nearly all phases of flight, including the landing.

The new technology has, however, also resulted in a range of new human factors and operational difficulties. New 'tools' have a way of changing how a job is done, and the new-technology aircraft is no exception. What has come to light from recent accidents involving advanced technology aircraft has been the fact that the technology can malfunction. It is also prone to human error.

Technology problem analysis

Major research into the operation of advanced technology aircraft has been conducted by many research, commercial and development groups in many advanced industrial countries. For human factors, there has been NASA in the USA and the Institute of Aviation Medicine at Farnborough, UK. These organisations have conducted field studies. There is no doubt the benefits that have been derived from automated technology are recognised internationally.

Now researchers are concerned about the safety issues connected with the operation of advanced technology aircraft.

Based on what has been discovered from research and past occurrences, the Safety Issues can be shown under various category headings. The following list shows possible Active Failures or Errors, defined as 'unsafe acts which could immediately precipitate an accident or incident':

- mode misapplication
- monitoring failures
- system 'workarounds'
- data entry errors

It is recognised that accidents or system breakdowns involving complex technological systems are rarely the result of an isolated error or unsafe act. One model of accident analysis stresses that accidents generally result from a combination of failures at all levels of the organisation from management down. In most cases, an accident is immediately precipitated by an unsafe act committed by an individual.

For the unsafe act to lead to an accident, there must be an inadequacy in system defences. The unsafe act may be either an error or a violation of standard procedures. What we can say is that unsafe acts do not occur in isolation, but in the context of error or violation, producing conditions such as haste, fatigue, or other psychological influences. In the context of advanced technology aircraft, these conditions may include:

- inadequate situational awareness
- inadequate systems awareness
- inadequate mode awareness
- automation over-reliance
- increased 'heads down' time (not looking outside enough)
- disrupted crew co-ordination

At an even higher level are organisational failures which have the potential to be relevant factors in an advanced technology-related incident. These include failures in management attitudes to operating efficiencies and training.

Chapter 2

What Crew Resource Management Training is All About

The requirements

The requirements are a natural development from the Human Factors (HF) Flight Crew Licence examinations introduced by the Authority's Flight Crew Licensing Department. They will bring the United Kingdom (UK) into line with the European and North American approach to the training of flightcrews.

The course – definition

This complex subject is referred to by a variety of names, such as Flight Deck Management or Cockpit Resource Management. For the purpose of these requirements, and to align the Authority with the Federal Aviation Administration (FAA) and the Joint Aviation Authorities (JAA), it will now be designated Crew Resource Management (CRM). The Authority's interpretation of CRM training for single- and multi-crew is as follows:

- a comprehensive scheme for improving crew performance
- a scheme that addresses the entire crew population
- a scheme that can be extended to all forms of crew training
- a scheme that concentrates on crew members' attitudes and behaviour, and makes individual decisions on how to improve teamwork, within the aircraft and with outside agencies
- a scheme that uses the crew as a unit of training

Crew Resource Management training is not:

- a quick fix that can be implemented overnight
- a training programme administered to only a few specialised cases
- a scheme that occurs independently of other ongoing training activities
- a scheme where crews are given a specific prescription on how to work with others on the flight deck
- another form of individually centred crew training

- a passive-lecture classroom course
- an attempt by management to dictate cockpit behaviour or to expose individuals' weaknesses

General considerations – components of crew resource management

Training awareness

- Situational Awareness
- Communication
- Problem-Solving
- Decision-Making – Considered Judgement
- Team Management
- Team – Review
- Stress Management
- Interpersonal Skills
- Conflict Resolution

Practice and review

- Critique
  Self-Assessment
  Peer Group
- Line Orientated Flight Training (LOFT)
- Video

Consolidation training

- One training session is inadequate
- CRM should be integrated into the total aircrew training programme
- CRM should be an integral part of long-term organisational planning and development
- Necessity for regular recurrent training programme, with emphasis on crew co-ordination and simulator scenarios

Crew Resource Management training is designed to address behaviour as a product of all the things that make you who you are: your overall knowledge, the way and what you think, personality, attitude and experience. All these elements influence your behaviour. Although CRM does not in any way concentrate on personality change, it can teach you ways to think clearly in group decision-making. This can obviously influence your attitude, inter-personal communication and leadership ability, as well as your reaction to stress.

ANNEXE

'MODEL' CREW RESOURCE MANAGEMENT (CRM) COURSE AND HUMAN FACTORS (HF) APPRECIATION

DAY 1

1 Introduction
Objective of the course
Definition of CRM

2 Statistical Authentication of CRM Requirement
(75% of all incidents)
Examples of HF-related accidents
Video/audio/reports/diagrams

3 HF – Human Perception
Visual Limitations
(eye-brain link)
- Illusions – landing, 'whiteout', cloud
- Airmiss and collision problems (Relate to item 2 above)

Aural Limitations
(ear-brain link)
- Purpose of semi-circular canals (Relate to item 2 above)

4 Skills Required by Pilot (Selection)
- * Psycho-motor
- Level of intelligence
- Personality type

DAY 2

8 Procedures and Standard Operating Procedures (SOP) (company)
- Rule-based – philosophy
- Checklists – (practice lists or checks)
- Benefits and drawbacks, of both types
- Emergency or abnormal procedures
- Does the emergency fit the checklist? (and vice-versa)

9 Flight Deck and Cabin Attendants Social Structure
- Causes of clash or conflict – listening
- Causes of reduced crew performance
- Examples-incidents-examples from CHIRP
- The notion of interpersonal skills
- Adult-to-adult relationships (parent/adult/child)
- Clash of cognitive styles

DAY 3

12 CRM Loop Expanded
Inquiry
- Right questions
- Collect and validate
- Continuous update and information
- Test Accuracy

Advocacy
- Frankly state opinion
- Express concerns
- Seeks others' ideas

Conflict Resolution
- Work out differences
- Look for reasons and causes
- Emphasise what is right, not who is right
- Clash of cognitive styles (Style of Leadership)

Decision-Making
- Arrive at sound and safe decisions
- Change mind when convinced
- Work for understanding and support of crew

- Personal qualities
- Leadership
- Team membership

5. HF – Learning Process
   - Memory and Recall
     Limitations of memory and recall
     Methods of learning (visual, aural tactile retention assisted by reinforcement)
   - Types of Knowledge
     Skill-based
     Rule-based
     Knowledge (technical)

6 HF – Stress
  * Definition
  Types
  - Physiological
  - Psychological
  - Over- or under-arousal
  Notion of stress accumulation (i.e. family, work, travel, bereavement)
  Stress management (relate to item 2 above)

7 Tiredness or Fatigue

The Development of a Professional Style

10. Case Study
  * • Documented accidents and incidents – Groups to investigate and make a presentation of findings.

11 The CRM Loop (outline)
  The notion of the right atmosphere (SOP, checklist discipline) (interpersonal skills)

  Inquiry
  Advocacy
  Conflict Resolution
  Decision-Making Critique
  FEEDBACK

  Notion of Synergy

- Team membership (lead/follow)

Critique
- Constructively review
- Plans and results
- Use feedback for learning
- Develop basis for improvement

13 Case Study (As Unit 10)
  * • Time-limited use of CRM Loop to produce findings by group presentation

14 Summary and Wash-Up
  - Frailty of human perception
  - Memory/recall
  - Performance (variability)
  - Need to be professional in CRM
  - Be realistically aware of human error – encourage openness

15 Course Critique

*Denotes Major Participation.

Dealing with stress is an important component of CRM, because one of its most significant greater effects is a degrading of verbal and other communication processes. What this training can also do is help you to be more flexible in how you handle difficult situations; then, even more importantly, help you to improve your ability to maximise resources in critical situations when effectiveness is a life-or-death issue.

HF/CRM is primarily flight safety training

We must grasp the fact that it is the pilot (aircrew) who is the ultimate 'back-stop', who will overcome all problems and emergency situations. Training helps reduce the frequency of human error implicit in this, and if there is to be any further major progress in flight safety, this can only be achieved by:

- a greater emphasis on understanding all the elements making up human factors
- an improved knowledge of human performance
- continual improvement in the selection and training of pilots
- wider industry co-operation in research and development for the next generation of aircraft

The most important means of recognising problems and risks in aviation, then limiting or avoiding them altogether, is to concentrate on:

- Crew Resource Management
- training
- practice
- teamwork
- using experience
- quality leadership by the captain

However, no real progress will be made unless 'aviation management' generally commits resources (time and finance) to long-term investment in flight safety. Running parallel with that, the flightcrew has to be suitably *educated* and *motivated* by the right 'trainers' so that the correct objectives will be achieved.

Industry and regulatory safety concerns

Crew Resource Management is regarded as a somewhat intangible subject. In some parts of the aviation industry it still attracts a certain level of distrust; certainly a subject that's all right for psychologists to play around with, but in general to be kept out of mainstream training.

Over the years manufacturing standards have improved, there's no doubt about that. Now more attention is being focused on the flightcrew. One of the reasons is that 70–75% of accidents and incidents have a high CRM/HF involvement, therefore CRM is the best area to target for improvement in accident prevention.

The boom and bust years of pilot training have thrown up their own set of problems within the aviation industry. In times of expansion it seemed that parts of the industry had forgotten how to train upcoming and low-experience pilots, particularly on subjects such as airmanship and Crew Resource Management. We have to realise that CRM is not there to replace basic skills. Basic skills, learning and testing should run in conjunction with CRM training.

One senior CAA source has highlighted several areas of particular concern. These include: 'altitude busts', conflict between military and civilian traffic, and controlled flight into terrain. Other considerations relate to:

- *Training:* must be adequate and cover all aspects of the operation
- *Flight time limitations:* to protect crew from fatigue
- *Operating conditions:* how crews are handled. Do they have proper facilities? For example, is there adequate time available to brief before each flight?
- *Unsafe practices among crews:* some stem directly from management, i.e. fuel policy, maintenance, ramp safety
- *Selection and promotion of pilots and engineers:* do not just select yes men because it's industrially convenient
- *Selection and purchase of aircraft:* suitability to route, and suitability of aircrew
- *Its application on a day-to-day basis:* reinforce benefits and lessons learned, i.e. use company newsletters for feedback. Listen to line checkers, base trainers. Target areas of unsafe practice. Have annual reviews.

The following extract from a National Transportation Safety Board Aircraft Accident report is presented as an example of how good Crew Resource Management training can play a major role in helping to deal with a catastrophic systems failure in the air, and influence the outcome of an extreme emergency situation.

United Airlines Flight 232, McDonnell Douglas DC-10-10, Sioux Gateway Airport, Sioux City, Iowa

19 July 1989

FACTUAL INFORMATION

United Airlines (UAL) flight 232 (UA 232), a McDonnell Douglas DC-10-10, registration no. N1819U, was a scheduled passenger flight from Stapleton

International Airport, Denver, Colorado, to Philadelphia, conducted under Title 14 Code of Federal Regulations (CFR) Part 121. Flight 232 departed Denver at 1409 central daylight time. There were 285 passengers and eleven crew members on board.

The take-off and the en route climb to the planned cruising altitude of 37,000 feet were uneventful. The first officer (co-pilot) was the flying pilot. The autopilot was engaged, and the autothrottles were selected in the speed mode for 270 KIAS. The flight plan called for a cruise speed of Mach 0.83.

About one hour and seven minutes after take-off, at 1516:10, the flightcrew heard a loud bang or an explosion followed by vibration and a shuddering of the airframe. After checking the engine instruments, the flightcrew determined that the No. 2 aft (tail-mounted) engine had failed (see Figure 1). The captain called for the engine shutdown checklist. While performing the engine shutdown checklist, the second officer (flight engineer) observed that the airplane's normal system hydraulic pressure and quantity gauges indicated zero.

The first officer advised that he could not control the airplane as it entered a right descending turn. The captain took control of the airplane and confirmed that it did not respond to flight control inputs. The captain reduced thrust on the No. 1 engine, and the airplane began to roll to a wings-level attitude. The flightcrew deployed the air-driven generator (ADG), which powers the No. 1 auxiliary hydraulic pump, and the hydraulic pump was selected 'on'. This action did not restore hydraulic power.

At 1520, the flightcrew radioed the Minneapolis Air Route Traffic Control Center (ARTCC) and requested emergency assistance and vectors to the nearest airport. Initially, Des Moines International Airport was suggested by ARTCC. At 1522, the air traffic controller informed the flightcrew that they were proceeding in the direction of Sioux City; the controller asked the flightcrew if they would prefer to go there. The flightcrew responded, 'Affirmative'. They were then given vectors to the Sioux Gateway Airport (SUX) at Sioux City, Iowa (see Figure 2).

Crew interviews indicate that shortly after the engine failure, the passengers were informed of the failure of the No. 2 engine, and the senior flight attendant was called to the cockpit. She was told to prepare the cabin for an emergency landing. She returned to the cabin and separately informed the other flight attendants to prepare for an emergency landing. A flight attendant advised the captain that a UAL DC-10 training check airman, who was off duty and seated in a first-class passenger seat, had volunteered his assistance. The captain immediately invited the airman to the cockpit, and he arrived at about 1529. At the request of the captain, the check airman entered the passenger cabin and performed a visual inspection of the airplane's wings. Upon his return, he reported that the inboard ailerons were slightly up, not damaged, and that the spoilers were locked down. There was no movement of

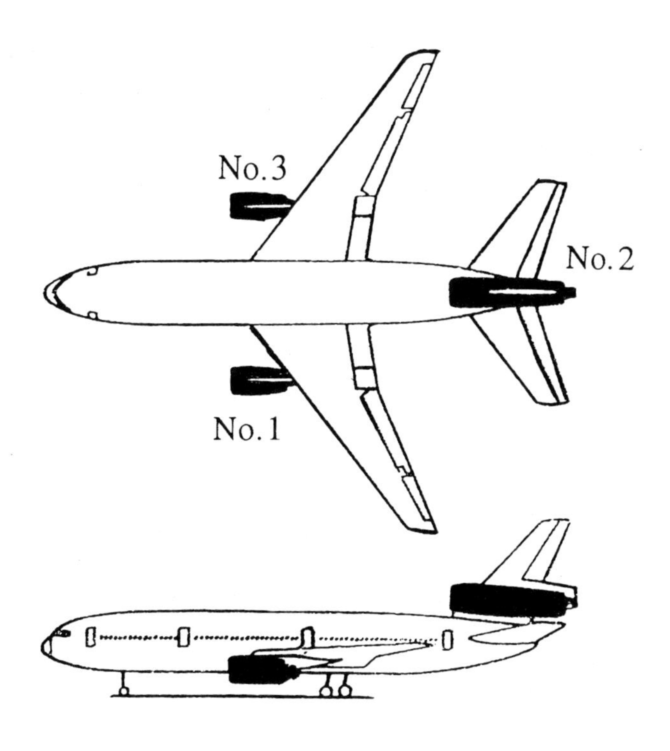

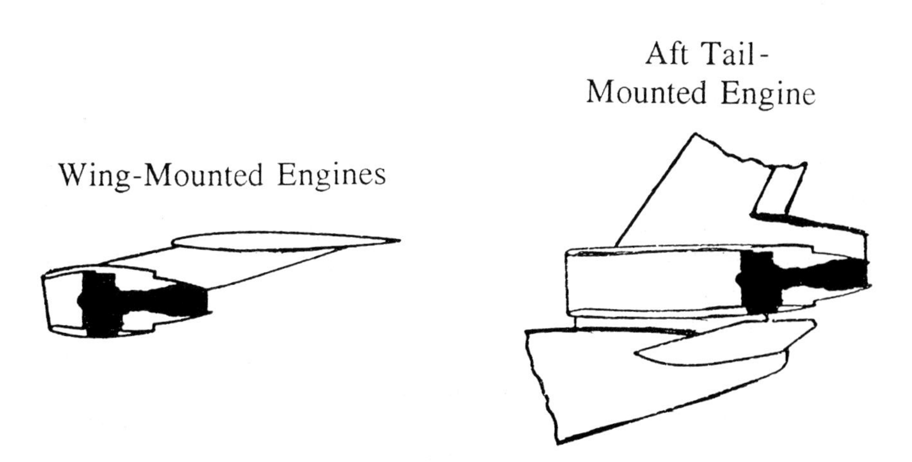

Figure 1 DC-10 aircraft view illustrated with engine arrangement

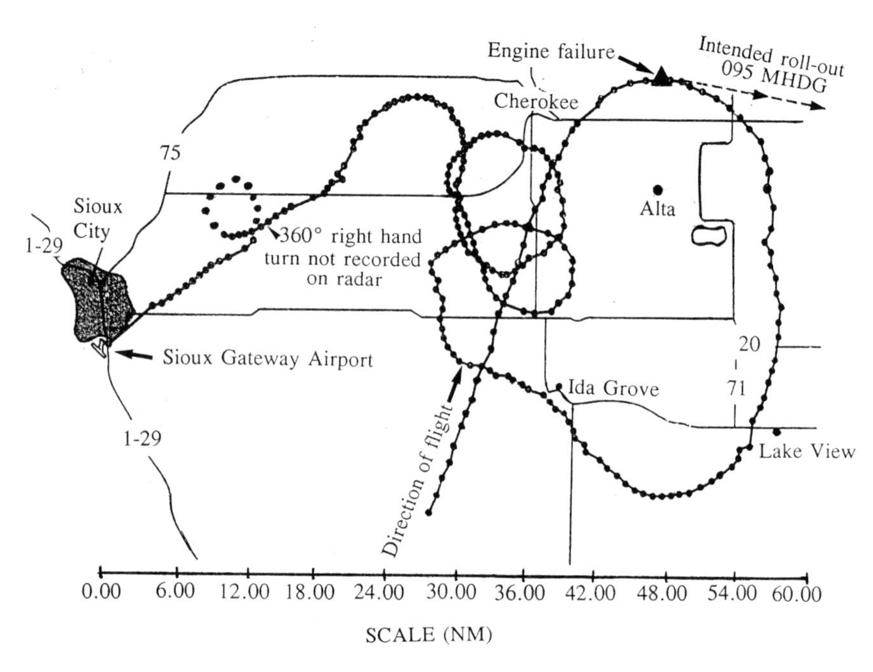

Figure 2 Ground track from radar plot

the primary flight control surfaces. The captain then directed the check airman to take control of the throttles to free the captain and first officer to manipulate the flight controls. The check airman attempted to use engine power to control pitch and roll. He said that the airplane had a continuous tendency to turn right, that the No. 1 and No. 3 engine thrust levers could not be used asymmetrically, so he used two hands to manipulate the two throttles.

About 1542, the second officer was sent to the passenger cabin to inspect the empennage visually. Upon his return, he reported that he observed damage to the right and left horizontal stabilisers.

Fuel was jettisoned to the level of the automatic system cut-off, leaving 33,500 pounds. About eleven minutes before landing, the landing gear was extended by means of the alternate gear extension procedure.

The flightcrew said that they made visual contact with the airport about nine miles out. ATC had intended for flight 232 to attempt to land on runway 31, which was 8,999 feet long. However, ATC advised that the airplane was on approach to runway 22, which was closed, and that the length of this runway was 6,600 feet. Given the airplane's position and the difficulty in making left turns, the captain elected to continue the approach to runway 22 rather than attempt a manoeuvre to runway 31. The check airman said that he believed the airplane was lined up and on a normal glidepath to the field. The flaps and slats remained retracted.

During the final approach, the captain recalled getting a high sink rate alarm from the ground proximity warning system (GPWS). In the last twenty seconds before touchdown, the airspeed averaged 215 KIAS, and the sink rate was 1,620 feet per minute. Smooth oscillations in pitch and roll continued until just before touchdown when the right wing dropped rapidly. The captain stated that about one hundred feet above the ground the nose of the airplane began to pitch downward. He also felt the right wing drop down about the same time. Both the captain and the first officer called for reduced power on short final approach.

The check airman said that based on experience with no flap/no slat approaches he knew that power would have to be used to control the airplane's descent. He used the first officer's airspeed indicator and visual cues to determine the flightpath and the need for power changes. He thought that the airplane was fairly well aligned with the runway during the latter stages of the approach and that they would reach the runway. Soon thereafter, he observed that the airplane was positioned to the left of the desired landing area and descending at a high rate. He also observed that the right wing began to drop. He continued to manipulate the No. 1 and No. 3 engine throttles until the airplane contacted the ground. He said that no steady application of power was used on the approach and that the power was constantly changing. He believed that he added power just before contacting the ground.

The airplane touched down on the threshold slightly to the left of the centreline on runway 22 at 1600. First ground contact was made by the right wing tip followed by the right main landing gear. The airplane skidded to the right of the runway and rolled to an inverted position. Witnesses observed the airplane ignite and cartwheel, coming to rest after crossing runway 17/35. Firefighting and rescue operations began immediately.

The accident occurred during daylight conditions at 42° 25′ north latitude and 96° 23′ west longitude.

Injuries to Persons

Injuries	Crew	Passengers	Others	Total
Fatal	1	110	0	111
Serious	6	41*	0	47
Minor	4	121	0	125
None	0	13	0	13
Total	11	285	0	296

*One passenger died thirty-one days after the accident as a result of the injuries he had received in the accident. In accordance with 49 CFR 830.2, his injuries were classified 'serious'.

The airplane was destroyed by impact and post-crash fire. Photographs of the airplane were taken by observers on the ground during its final approach to Sioux Gateway Airport. They showed that the No. 2 engine fan cowling and the fuselage tail cone were missing. The remainder of the No. 2 engine appeared intact. Post-crash examination of the wreckage revealed that the No. 2 engine fan rotor components forward of the fan forward shaft, as well as part of the shaft, had separated from the engine in flight.

The airplane's right wing began to break up immediately following touchdown. The remainder of the airplane broke up as it tumbled down the runway. The fuselage centre section, with most of the left wing still attached, came to rest in a corn field after crossing runway 17/35. The cockpit separated early in the sequence and came to rest at the edge of runway 17/35. The largely intact tail section continued down runway 22 and came to rest on taxiway 'L'. The engines separated during the break-up. The No. 1 and No. 3 engines came to rest near taxiway 'L' and the intersection of runway 17/35, between 3,000 and 3,500 feet from the point of first impact. The No. 2 engine came to rest on taxiway 'J' to the left of runway 22, about 1,850 feet from the point of first impact. The majority of the No. 2 engine fan module was not found at the airport.

The value of the airplane was estimated at $21,000,000.

Documentation and analysis of the No. 2 engine components and surrounding structure led the Safety Board to conclude that the No. 2 engine stage 1 fan disk fracture and separation was the initial event that led to the liberation of engine rotating parts with sufficient energy to penetrate the airplane's structure.

Shortly after the engine failure, the crew noted that the hydraulic fluid pressure and quantity had fallen to zero in the three systems. Approximately one minute after the engine failure, the FDR recorded no further powered movement of the flight control surfaces. Consequently, the No. 2 engine failure precipitated severe damage that breached the three hydraulic systems, leaving the flight control systems inoperative. Titanium alloy was found on the fracture surfaces of severed lines of hydraulic systems No. 1 and No. 3 located in the right horizontal stabiliser. Several of the major components of the engine, including the stage 1 fan blades and fan disk, were made from titanium alloy and no other components of the surrounding airframe were made from such material. These factors led the Safety Board to conclude that the system's No. 1 and No. 3 hydraulic lines were severed by fragments released during the failure sequence of the No. 2 engine.

The loss of hydraulic system No. 2 required further analysis. The engine-driven No. 2 hydraulic pumps were attached to and received power from the No. 2 engine accessory section. This unit was mounted to the engine directly below the fan section of the engine. Portions of the No. 2 engine accessory section and associated No. 2 hydraulic system components, including hydraulic supply hoses, were found in the Alta, Iowa area. Therefore, portions of the No. 2 hydraulic system and supply hoses mounted on, or adjacent to, the No. 2 engine accessory section were damaged and separated by the forces and disruption of the engine fan section during the engine failure. The investigation disclosed no evidence of other system anomalies that would have contributed to the hydraulic system or flight control difficulties experienced in the accident.

Because of the loss of the three hydraulic systems, the flightcrew was confronted with a unique situation that left them with very limited control of the airplane. The only means available to fly the airplane was through manipulation of thrust available from the No. 1 and No. 3 engines. The primary task confronting the flightcrew was controlling the airplane on its flightpath during the long period (about sixty seconds) of the 'phugoid' or pitch oscillation. This task was extremely difficult to accomplish because of the additional need to use the No. 1 and No. 3 power levers asymmetrically to maintain lateral (roll) control coupled with the need to use increases and decreases in thrust to maintain pitch control. The flightcrew found that despite their best efforts, the airplane would not maintain a stabilised flight condition.

Douglas Aircraft Company, the FAA, and UAL considered the total loss of hydraulic-powered flight controls so remote as to negate any requirement for an appropriate procedure to counter such a situation. The most comparable manoeuvre that the flightcrew was required to accomplish satisfactorily in a DC-10 simulator was the procedure for managing the failure of two of the three hydraulic systems; however, during this training the remaining system was available for movement of the flight controls.

The CVR recorded the flightcrew's discussion of procedures, possible solutions, and courses of action in dealing with the loss of hydraulic system flight controls, as well as the methods of attempting an emergency landing. The captain's acceptance of the check airman to assist in the cockpit was positive and appropriate.

The Safety Board views the interaction of the pilots, including the check airman, during the emergency as indicative of the value of cockpit resource management training, which has been in existence at UAL for a decade.

The loss of the normal manner of flight control, combined with an airframe vibration and the visual assessment of the damage by crew members, led the flightcrew to conclude that the structural integrity of the airplane was in jeopardy and that it was necessary to expedite an emergency landing. Interaction between the flightcrew and the UAL system aircraft maintenance (SAM) network did not lead to beneficial guidance. UAL flight operations attempted to ask the flightcrew to consider diverting to Lincoln, Nebraska. However, the information was sent through flight dispatch and did not reach the flightcrew in time to have altered their decision to land at the Sioux Gateway Airport.

The simulator re-enactment of the events leading to the crash-landing revealed that line flightcrews could not be taught to control the airplane and land safely without hydraulic power available to operate the flight controls. The results of the simulator experiments showed that a landing attempt under these conditions involves many variables that affect the extent of controllability during the approach and landing. In general, the simulator re-enactments indicated that landing parameters such as speed, touchdown point, direction, attitude, or vertical velocity could be controlled separately, but it was virtually impossible to control all parameters simultaneously.

After carefully observing the performance of a control group of DC-10-qualified pilots in the simulator, it became apparent that training for an attempted landing comparable to that experienced by UA 232 would not help the crew to successfully handle this problem. Therefore, the Safety Board concludes that the damaged DC-10 airplane, although flyable, could not have been successfully landed on a runway with the loss of all hydraulic flight controls.

The Safety Board believes that under the circumstances the UAL flightcrew performance was highly commendable and greatly exceeded reasonable expectations.

CHAPTER 3
COCKPIT RESOURCE MANAGEMENT

PART 1 – CONCEPTS

This refers to the effective use of all resources within the scope of the cockpit (flight deck) environment, to achieve safe and efficient flight operations. It is a part of the wider concept of Practical Cockpit Management.

It could also be said to be an extension of pilot judgement for multi-crew aircraft. The primary focus is on communication, both interactive between the flightcrew, and with outside sources such as Air Traffic Control. Communication is a key factor in CRM, because this is how such 'management' is achieved. Many General Aviation aircraft fly with two pilots, so CRM is perfectly relevant in this context, as indeed it is between flight instructor and student pilot. The principles involved are helpful in improving the effective cockpit management techniques and safety. CRM provides a sound basis for all pilots who intend moving up into larger aircraft. It helps establish teamwork and communication skills that can be carried through the learning and experience-gathering process.

Importance of flying skills

Before we look at the training aspect, we have to arrive at some conclusions. One is that the pilot(s) involved have the necessary technical flying skills; in other words they are actually able to fly an aircraft. Therefore we are not involved in discussing or teaching flying skills. Secondly, we are not being selective with regard to the individual personality. Obviously this does to some extent affect crew management performance, but CRM makes no attempt to change the personality of the individual involved in CRM training; rather, it encourages a pilot to think effectively in group (multi-crew) decision-making, and to make an impression on subsequent attitudes, inter-personal crew relationships and leadership. There can be more flexibility in handling the more difficult situations, and in utilising available resources to the best, and safest, advantage in life-and-death emergencies.

What is CRM training?

The primary objective is to promote effective decision-making, with the key objective being communication among all crew members. The captain is the recognised team leader. He or she must request any required information. The answers must be freely given in a way that facilitates sound decision-making, which means the development of inter-personal communication skills. It is essential to develop 'Team Concepts' that will deal with problems and stress. Stress and stressors are dealt with in some detail in this book. The inability to deal with stress leads to a reduction in overall performance and interactive communication.

Attitudes to management versus personality

In Cockpit Management, attitudes can be modified through training; so can personal attitudes up to a point, but severe personality disorders have no place anywhere in aviation.Very few pilots have any extremes of personality that would affect safety in the cockpit, and those that have are soon removed from the aviation scene.

Personality means the characteristics you developed or acquired in early life. It is the strategy we develop to accomplish ambitions and deal with the people around us.

Attitudes are elements of our personality and are easily subject to change, especially from a variety of outside influences around us. We can be affected by advertising, politicians, teachers, our own family and many other things.

How flying tasks affect relationships

We are all concerned as to how our attitude affects others we work with, even if we sometimes believe that others do not care. Every individual has a concern about successfully completing the task in hand.

A certain amount of assertiveness in a command pilot is desirable as it produces the best overall results in decision-making. Whatever else you may feel, the approach to the demands of cockpit management should avoid any extremes of attitude, personality traits, aggressiveness, or anything else which will disrupt harmony in the cockpit and your role in it. Emergencies or critical situations will require various combinations of assertive or aggressive style. This is simply because there is little or no time to consider the finer points of relationships or seek further information that may or may not be of use.

Sometimes, however, other situations may need a 'diplomatic-assertive' style, such as assisting inexperienced crew members through a stressful period or an inadvertent mistake. It is equally important that other crew members should understand how you work and behave at all times. From this, confidence is built and trust is established.

In general terms it is more advantageous to adopt a basically assertive style. Any extremes of behaviour can lead to a breakdown in inter-crew relationships, and particularly communication.

Inter-personal communication

This is the most important aspect of CRM training, because without it conducting Cockpit Management procedures becomes totally impossible.

It is the responsibility of each individual crew member to make quite certain he or she is communicating effectively. This means a whole lot more than using the correct aviation phraseology, or enunciating words clearly and correctly over the radio and intercom (many don't bother and it can cause crew confusion). What it also means in the wider sense is making sure the other person(s) *understand* what is being said. Analyse your own communication style, as well as those of others, and see how or if it needs improving.

If we look closely at the various factors involved in communication, we can see how they deal with the transfer of information vital to the recipient's understanding:

- proficiency in seeking information
- stating your case; fluency in imparting the information
- listening to what is happening and the information being given
- solving problems or conflict within the cockpit
- exercising effective leadership, sometimes called the provision of an effective critique of fellow crew members; this helps overall decision-making and managing resources

It is important you understand these concepts so that you can alter and use them in your own everyday cockpit communications.

Proficiency in seeking information

This is the start point in the process of making effective decisions. To make good decisions you need good information. This comes from a variety of sources: visual, other crew members, sources outside the cockpit (ATC), maps and charts plus technical data in operations and flight manuals. Anything that is not understood should be clarified immediately. A good insight into the personalities of other crew members is essential, particularly new or inexperienced pilots who may be reluctant to give information (nervousness, fear of peer ridicule). No crew member should ever be afraid to ask questions. A number of accidents could have been averted if more direct questions had been asked; the Tenerife disaster, for example, when the 747 flight engineer told the captain he believed the other (conflicting) 747 was still backtracking the active runway. The FE was not assertive enough and it appeared the captain was not concerned – he should have been and should have sought the information that could have avoided the disaster. There are several variations of what really happened – this is only one – but it makes the point.

Stating your case

Being assertive, but not overly so, in stating what you believe. Maintaining your position in what you believe to be correct. Many crew members have expressed concern over the actions of their captains in safety-threatening situations. In several well-known accidents, the captain would have benefited if the other crew member had been more forceful in pressing his opinion, or stating it more clearly. The lesson from this is to make your opinions known, to make *sure* you are communicating.

Listening to what is happening

Certainly a vital part of CRM. If no one is actually taking the trouble to listen, there will be a failure of communications. Listening requires effort. It also means asking clarifying questions along the way, responding and, if necessary, disagreeing. Communication is a two-way affair and listening is one part of it.

If you are a good listener, you most likely have the following attributes:

- you ask sensible and pertinent questions
- your demeanour is friendly, positive and encouraging; it shows co-operativeness
- you look the other person in the eye, and concentrate on what they are saying – not allowing your attention to wander on to something else that is happening around you
- you make sure you understand the speaker's position

Of course, all this results in better communication, helps inter-personal relationships, creates more harmony and co-operation in the cockpit, and above all contributes to safe and efficient practices.

Solving problems or conflict

Everyone in the cockpit has a position. Problems and conflict are inevitable, human nature being what it is, therefore there must always be a way of resolving these conflicts. And not all conflicts are necessarily bad. There can be healthy debate about cockpit management policies, responsibilities and other issues relevant to the cockpit.

What must be avoided are destructive personality issues that mostly originate outside the cockpit. Any argument can be fraught with additional problems when it is over *who* is right, rather than *what* is right. All this has a serious effect on morale, it focuses attention on irrelevant issues and reflects on the quality of subsequent decision-making.

Looking at it another way, conflict/problem-solving, whatever you want to call it, can be constructive. But it has to be handled in the right way. A captain can resolve 'conflict' with good results by following a few simple guidelines:

- during conflict, keep the solving of those issues within the cockpit
- give other crew members adequate opportunity to express their opinions and feelings
- make sure all the areas of disagreement are covered
- make sure your other crew members know how you feel; highlight your main concerns.

Proper problem solving and conflict resolution techniques lead to a better mutual respect within the cockpit and strengthen the team proficiency. Conflict resolution should therefore be used as an opportunity to find better solutions to problems and to improve communication.

Exercising effective leadership

Resolving problems and conflicts is one thing, exercising effective leadership thereafter is another. This is particularly so after criticising another crew member's performance, or discussing a mistake. To improve all the cockpit management skills, continual feedback by way of critique is necessary from all crew members.

Captains are the recognised leaders, but they often do not get the right feedback concerning their own performance, especially if they are check captains themselves. CRM training is a useful way of doing it.

Adequate pre-flight and post-flight briefings should always be given by the captain. It can help resolve misunderstandings, and also prevent important issues from being covered up. It is necessary for a captain to get feedback from others to form an accurate picture of his/her own performance. A cockpit leader should also be a competent and skilful pilot.

Responsibility, decisiveness, decision-making

A leader should have all these skills. Responsibility must be number one, as it comes above personal desires. Decisiveness is essential in the leader of a team environment. It helps influence unity of action. Any effective leader must be skilful in analysing problems, using information and then making a decision. Decision-making ability is therefore a vital ingredient in any command pilot's make-up. It can be developed through experience, knowledge and understanding the value of 'pattern recognition'.

The cockpit team and task delegation

The flightcrew team must work together to accomplish the job of flying the aircraft safely from A to B. If that team is not pulling together (individuals are working separately) then cohesion will be lost and safety jeopardised.

Large transport aircraft need a multi-crew operation simply to share the workload. This is to ensure the tasks are all performed in a timely and effective way. The 'team spirit' is instilled in pilots from their student pilot days, starting with the instructor-student relationship. Initially it can be difficult being part of a team, because humans are all basically 'individually' orientated.

With aircraft flightcrews, it is the (collective) crew that is evaluated and scrutinised when accidents occur, or in simulated practice. It is the performance of the team that counts. By developing this teamwork from the beginning, individual crew members develop the necessary habit of co-operation rather than competition. There is no place for competition in the cockpit. The captain, or leader, motivates his team to accomplish team goals over individual goals (unless the task is one of improving proficiency within the team concept). Delegating tasks is an essential part of a cockpit leader's ability in controlling the team. The captain, as leader, must therefore be flexible in his plans to deal with changes. This is a prime area where communication is important. The parameters of delegated responsibilities must be clearly defined:

- who is responsible for accomplishing each task
- the standard required
- priorities
- evaluation of the available resources to complete the task(s)

No single crew member of the team should be given a task beyond his/her capabilities, experience or relevant qualifications. Tasks delegated should be discreetly monitored as required. If mistakes are made, these may be discussed and corrected constructively.

Summary and Conclusion

Cockpit Resource Management is now recognised throughout the aviation industry (GA and airlines) as being an important component of safe flight. It is hoped that CRM techniques, when learned and practised, can and will reduce the number of accidents and incidents. These have been mainly caused by a breakdown of communication and decision-making capabilities.

An effective pilot-in-command is one who has certain traits and attributes:

- recognises the captain's training role for other flightcrew members
- is aware of the need for harmony in inter-personal relationships on the flight deck
- encourages other crew members to express their opinions on operational matters
- knows the importance of fully briefing other crew members, including cabin attendants
- has an acceptable and understandable plan for dealing with emergencies; how the appropriate checklist will be handled
- has an appropriately balanced assertive style of command that is understood by other crew members
- recognises personal limitations that minimise risk-taking
- communicates effectively in every situation

A captain who is ineffective faces many largely self-imposed problems. The most dangerous trait is the 'Rambo' complex in which risk-taking is a way of life and certainly detrimental to safety. This type has an authoritarian style of cockpit management which makes for tense, stressful situations and poor team co-ordination. The team is resentful and nervous about expressing opinions.

All the main elements of CRM are applicable to General Aviation. Try them out in your own operational environment.

CHAPTER 4

COCKPIT RESOURCE MANAGEMENT

PART 2 – PRACTICAL MANAGEMENT ISSUES AND SITUATIONAL AWARENESS

Definition of Cockpit Management

Cockpit Management, by whatever title and form, is the use and co-ordination of all the resources and skills available to the flight crew to achieve and maintain situational awareness. By doing this, we reach the objective of safety, efficiency and comfort during each flight.

Always establish who is flying the aircraft

That statement is not as odd as it might seem, because we always want to know who is controlling what. It relates to the identification process in knowing what is going on at all times in and outside the cockpit. This is known as situational awareness, and is one of the most important aspects of flying. It encompasses the entire spectrum of factors and conditions that affect the aircraft and flight-crew during any one specific period of time. It applies to every crew member, individually and collectively. It is a concept taught to student pilots from the beginning of flight training. It therefore follows that there is a direct relationship between situational awareness and safety management. There is no doubt that pilots who have better situational awareness are safer.

Individual situational awareness

As we can see, situational awareness is influenced by the individual. If we take a two-pilot crew, for example, one may have a very high level of awareness while the other is low, and of course there will even be small variations of situational awareness between highly aware crew members. So, as we analyse situational awareness, it is apparent there are variations because every human being is different.

Captain Starlight: 'I've been considering this latest company memo asking for suggestions about additional *cockpit resources*. Let's see, two new coffee cup holders, a microwave for crew lunches, a subscription to TIME magazine. What else . . .?'

Let's look at an IFR, two-pilot public transport flight heading for a destination airport surrounded by mountains. The captain has inadvertently descended well below the minimum safe sector altitude and the aircraft is on a collision course with a mountain peak five miles distant. Imagine what effect situational awareness might have on the outcome. The co-pilot is young, straight out of flight school with minimum experience, but because of recent training he has a high situational awareness and can see the dangerous position the aircraft is in. The captain, who is flying the aircraft, has been over the route so many times he has become complacent and bored. We all know about the classic 'familiarity breeds mistakes' syndrome. There is also another factor adding to the problems. He is thinking about a local golf tournament he is playing in the following day, which is important to him. Here is a combination of circumstances that has lowered his personal situational awareness to the point where he has made a potentially fatal error. Unless immediate action is taken the aircraft will crash. This is because *group* situational awareness is low, limited by the captain.

Group awareness

To enable the level of group awareness to be raised, the young co-pilot must intervene and impart his high level of situational awareness to the captain so that he will accept it. This is the most vital factor to achieving group situational awareness. There is no doubt that communication and a proper understanding of the concepts of command and leadership are essential.

International regulations recognise that 'the pilot in command of an aircraft is directly responsible for, and is the final authority, as to the operation of the aircraft'. But there is a fine line between being in charge and being dictatorial. Unfortunately, there have been instances where captains have crossed that line with disastrous results. Here are two well-documented examples.

One of the worst ever aviation accidents, which claimed 581 lives, was in part due to a captain who did not heed the warning of a subordinate flight-crew member. It was a prime example of the breakdown of group situational awareness. It was the KLM 747 at Tenerife Airport we mentioned earlier. Another example: the captain of Air Florida Flight 90 ignored several warnings from his co-pilot that the engine gauges 'didn't look right' during their take-off roll from snowbound Washington National Airport. The 737 in question crashed shortly after take-off.

While the co-pilot by definition is the subordinate crew member, or second in command, the captain should not be overbearing, although many are. As a Training Captain of many years' experience, I have checked out scores of pilots. One day I had just completed a young co-pilot's line training and released him for normal duties. An hour later I accidentally overheard a senior line captain telling the same co-pilot that when he was on board the aircraft he was to 'just sit in the (RH) seat, make the radio calls and shut up!' The captain was certainly not making the situation better for himself. He was actually increasing his own workload and wasting a valuable asset. Such a well-trained co-pilot could have substantially reduced his workload. Not only that, but the captain's situational awareness would also be lowered, thus decreasing group situational awareness. This self-imposed involvement in task performance restricts the available time for the important pilot-in-command duties of planning, analysis and decision-making.

Experience and training

What we mean by experience is the practical knowledge, skill, or increased expertise derived from training or direct observation of particular activities. We use different parts of this experience every time we fly. This experience is stored away in our brain's memory file. It helps us establish how changing conditions and events are interpreted and how we respond to them.

We are constantly reaching into this memory file of experience to guide the actions we take while we are flying, and to assess the different situations we face. This wealth of experience allows us to solve our problems more quickly and therefore allocate more time to other tasks which require a pilot's attention. Experience and training are therefore closely related. Training is much more than the effort to improve our system's knowledge and hone our physical flying skills. Training adds to our bank of experience.

A great many of the problems faced by pilots are actually solved before entering the aircraft. In the air, the constant review of certain emergency procedures is made easier as a result of repetitive training experience. For instance, dealing with a simulated engine failure on take-off at V2 becomes automatic to the well-trained pilot. Modern simulators allow us to recreate the worst-scenario in-flight emergency situations we could face in everyday flying. This contributes to our experience file without risking death or crashing the aircraft. When actual malfunctions occur, we can instantly draw on this experience for correct reactions.

Physical flying skills

We can all remember our days as student pilots. I learned to fly in an open-cockpit biplane with an ex-RAF WWII bomber pilot as my instructor. His highly developed situational awareness had been forged in the heat of aerial combat. He was a hard taskmaster even at my stage of flying experience.

Virtually all my attention was devoted to simply controlling the aircraft. I had little time to look out for other aircraft, navigate, or mull over the finer points of a developing weather situation. Consequently I can now see that my own level of situational awareness was extremely low. Many of us are only here today because our situational awareness was just sufficient to cope with the problems faced during this early period. My salvation was the ex-RAF instructor with his highly developed instinct for survival. His favourite expression was, 'Make that same mistake when you're solo and you'll kill yourself for sure!' He made the point that 'in wartime flying, there was no room for two mistakes'. Believe me, my learning curve in those circumstances was very rapid – especially in a tail dragger with a metal skid, no radio or brakes.

As our physical flying skills improve we are able to devote more time to the mental aspects of flying. We must continue to sharpen these skills to ensure that more of our energies are devoted to other important flying tasks. However much we develop, though, our physical flying skills are still very important.

Health and motivational attitude

A great many physical and emotional factors contribute to our capability in reaching and maintaining a high level of situational awareness. Therefore, our physical and emotional state directly affects our personal view and interpretation of events around us. Even a slight illness, or a combination of personal problems, can have a detrimental effect on our ability to function properly in a demanding flight environment. The stressful interview with the bank manager concerning your overdraft which takes place just one hour before arriving at the airport must be forgotten. It is a fact that good emotional and physical health is essential for establishing and sustaining high levels of situational awareness. Also, a good professional attitude allows us to focus our energies in a more positive manner. It is every pilot's own personal commitment to safety, that furthers situational awareness.

How to apply situational awareness

If no one is flying the aircraft or looking out of the cockpit window, situational awareness is severely compromised; unattended and uncorrected deviations become a very real possibility. Even when the autopilot is engaged, any aircraft needs a pilot, or pilots, to 'mind the shop' *inside* and *outside* the cockpit.

As we have seen, a pilot establishes situational awareness through training and good cockpit management skills. This involves setting specific targets for each and every flight. These targets then become the yardstick by which we measure situational awareness. Once these parameters have been established, they are maintained by detecting and correcting any deviations. The key to continuing a high level of situational awareness lies in closely monitoring progress and making sure no problems arise. This is very important, as there is no formal measure of situational awareness. It is important for flightcrews to recognise the clues that will highlight any actual or possible loss of situational awareness. The following are some of the main ones:

Failure to meet planned targets This could mean higher than expected fuel consumption, ETAs not met, or failure to achieve cruise performance. If these are not analysed and acted upon, situational awareness will inevitably be compromised.

Ambiguity Takes place any time two or more different sources of information disagree. It can include different readings for the same aircraft system from two separate sources, navigation, electronics, etc., or uncertainty of posi-

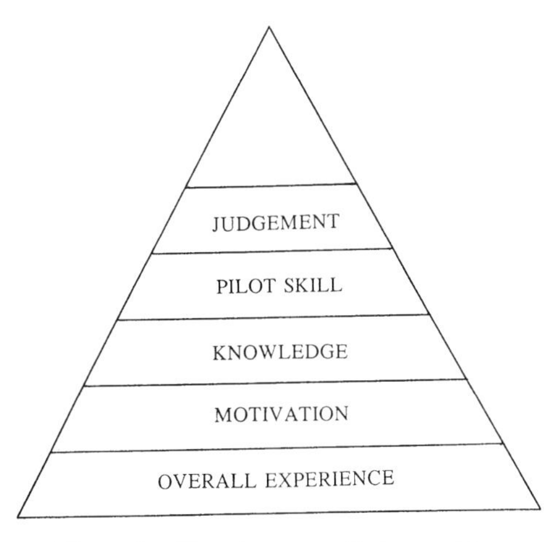

Figure 3 The elements of airmanship

tion deviating from the flight plan. As long as such ambiguities exist, are ignored or unresolved, situational awareness is in danger.

Mental confusion A sudden increase in unnecessary stress causing doubts which impair judgement. Our conscious mind can suppress our subconscious doubts to a great extent, or our personal ability to handle them. Any doubt can lead to a loss of situational awareness if it cannot be resolved or overcome.

Improper procedures This involves aircraft systems, violation of air traffic control and approach procedures, and operating outside the safe and efficient flight envelope of the aircraft. Any time improper or totally non-standard procedures are even considered, situational awareness suffers and this can become a major element in aviation safety. Thus, establishing and minimising its loss is accomplished by good cockpit management.

Summary of situational awareness

Definition Situational awareness is the accurate perception of the factors and actual conditions that affect the aircraft and the flightcrew during any specific period of time. In short, it is knowing what is going on around you.

Experience This helps to create a mental file which each pilot can access before and during every flight. It plays a major part in decision-making. Under pressure, human behaviour tends to revert to previous patterns. The individual's experience file helps to establish how that human being will interpret and then respond to a given set of conditions.

Physical flying skills With, or because of, advancing aviation technology, the pilot's role in the cockpit has become one of systems computer manager. The aircraft is controlled by the technology watched by the pilot. The one thing we have to remember is that pilots must still be able to physically fly the aircraft proficiently. Manual control will continue to be an important and indispensable part of a pilot's job.

Training This does far more than hone and improve skills, it adds valuable information to a pilot's experience file. In a flight simulator, for example, it is easy to recreate emergency situations that would not be safe to perform in the air, and those that would happen only rarely in the real world of flying. Through training, all these events can measurably add to a pilot's experience. Then if the worst happens there will be pre-knowledge that can be used.

Information processing This is the ability to use information from *sense* inputs, i.e. instruments and other indicators that give an accurate picture of what is happening.

Spatial orientation We can define this as 'position awareness'. In other words, where the aircraft is in relation to navaids such as VORs, NDBs, etc., terrain (lowest safe altitude to fly), altitudes in general, the aircraft aptitude and other aircraft. It relates to the aircraft's actual position and knowing where you are going.

Cockpit management ability Skills in this area add considerably to a pilot's overall ability to manage the whole of the flight environment.

Personal attitude Our professionalism is a matter of attitude. If we consider safety, it doesn't just happen. Each pilot (crew) has to work at it to make it happen. If you think safe, the chances are you will be safe.

Physical and emotional condition Each individual's physical and emotional condition affects his/her perception of the environment. What can really affect the overall human equation are emotional problems, below-par physical condition, mental illness, even a pilot's frame of mind. This negative attitude in relation to flying can affect and alter a pilot's accurate perception of (operational) events and general (flying) conditions. All these elements, therefore, make a contribution to overall situational awareness. The one thing we must understand above all else is that the pilot controls them.

Situational awareness

1. Give brief details of an instance when you consider your situational awareness was:
   a) at a very low level
   b) at a very high level
2. In your opinion, what has been the worst barrier to achieving and maintaining a high level of situational awareness?
3. What cockpit management techniques do you use to reach and maintain good situational awareness?
4. Do you have a self-warning technique that helps you detect reduced situational awareness?

Practical cockpit management

Practical cockpit management could equally fall under the heading of Managing Cockpit Safety. It is a wide and involved subject with many different facets that every pilot should understand better. Unfortunately, a large percentage of pilots do not give it the attention it deserves and they are the poorer for it. So whatever emphasis you want to place on this 'management', it goes well beyond the actual physical flying.

In the aviation industry's quest for safety, attention has been focused on the more obvious deficiencies, such as mechanical failures and bad errors in airmanship. Maybe this is an over-simplistic approach to the problems; you might ask yourself why perfectly competent pilots suddenly make mistakes in misreading approach charts, or unaccountably fly below a sector safety altitude. Flying is a complex, interwoven series of tasks that is constantly subjected to what researchers describe as the 'human factor' in aviation safety. Theoretically, there are four types of errors:

- performance of a required task incorrectly
- performance of a proper task at the wrong time
- performance of an improper action
- failure to perform a required task

However, in recent years a better understanding of human interaction and behavioural patterns has emerged. This is helping to solve some unanswered questions relating to accidents, as well as focusing attention on ways to improve operational safety and efficiency. It has led to a greater understanding of the way people behave individually and collectively, whether under stress or not. Pilots need to be re-informed of the problems and how to manage and overcome them.

The result of compound mistakes

In flying, disaster is normally the consequence of compound mistakes. For example, a landing gear fails to extend and during the troubleshooting period the aircraft is rendered unrecoverable through a series of unfortunate mistakes by both pilots. Firstly, the co-pilot drops the (emergency) checklist on the cockpit floor and it slides behind the seat out of reach. In the process of trying to retrieve the checklist he accidentally disengages the autopilot. At the same time the impatient, stressed captain, whose prime responsibility is to fly the aircraft, takes unilateral action to deal with the situation without the emergency checklist (forgetting there is one on his side of the cockpit). He inadvertently shuts off the LP fuel cock to the left engine (the most critical of his turbo-prop aircraft); the lever is right next to the emergency gear extension handle (both coloured red). Naturally the left engine stops.

Neither the problem with the landing gear, the dropping of the checklist, nor the unexpected disengagement of the autopilot should have caused the aircraft to crash. It was the *cumulative* effect of stress resulting in panic-induced impatience, resulting in a severe loss of situational awareness and a total breakdown of normal cockpit management.You might say that such a series of mistakes could not happen, but there are many well-documented accident reports which highlight similar chains of events.

None of us can say how we will react as individual pilots when faced with a real emergency. This is why repetitive training, and awareness training, is so vitally important. I feel sorry for the over-confident pilot who tells me that all the training he has had to do is an over-rated waste of time – *he* hasn't experienced *any* emergency in twenty-five years of flying. In my opinion, that pilot is a liability.

When faced with an emergency, even if initially you simply remember just to fly and control the aircraft until the heart rate is under control, then you are well on the way to survival. Training conditions the mind to act correctly to the (emergency) situation; but it is only self-motivation and a positive mental attitude that will lift us into the high state of situational awareness necessary to handle our professional flying responsibilities. As on every take-off, *think* emergency and if it happens you are in a positive mental attitude to deal with it effectively.

There have been classic examples of pilots selecting the wrong fuel tank in the wrong sequence, and even shutting off the fuel in flight as mentioned in the previous example. There are known instances of pilots failing to do anything at all and consequently running a tank dry. When these errors, or potential errors, are considered and measured against known weaknesses in the aircraft, crew or the operational environment, the pilot is better able to

Captain Starlight: 'MEA, MDA, DH – what next? It was never as complicated as this in 1943. I remember flying everywhere at 200 feet!'

avoid these compound tragedies. No flightcrew is morally responsible for the failures of others, but the cockpit can be regarded as the last line of defence, and a simple review of potential errors can easily highlight the most critical items.

There are many important skills which contribute to good cockpit management. These skills can be learned and practised and apply in varying degrees to all pilots irrespective of aircraft type or qualifications. Here are eight major areas relating to cockpit management which it would be advantageous for every flight crew member to study and analyse in relation to their own operation:

- cockpit distractions – imposed or random
- correct use and function of checklists
- workload assessment – time and stress management
- decision-making relating to sound aviation judgement
- inter-personal management skills – communication
- managing cockpit resources
- flight planning in all its aspects
- chain events (pattern recognition)

The Safety Window

The rapid changes in aircraft technology have brought about changes for all pilots, from that of control manipulator to an information processor. Only with a programme of integrated training can we assimilate new skills and let the new technologies blend in and take the place of old ones. But even with the new technology accidents still occur. Let's look at the most vulnerable phase of flight in which the majority of accidents happen.

The diagrammatic view (Fig 4) shows us the 'Safety Window', which is a block of airspace extending from ground level to 2,000 feet AGL. This is centred around a runway with the 'window' beginning at or around a final approach fix, extending to the end of the final segment of take-off climb. As we show, it is also the period of highest accident potential. A closely interwoven use of cockpit management skills and situational awareness is necessary throughout the Safety Window period. For a conventional turbo-prop or jet aircraft the window is about four to six minutes long, and of the accidents involving professional pilots, eighty-three per cent occur within this window. Ninety per cent of these accidents are generic, meaning their cause is not confined to a specific weight category or particular type. For instance, the failure of the crew to extend the landing gear will result in a wheels-up landing irrespective of aircraft type. Statistics show that generic accidents tend to be caused by pilots, rather than as a result of any technical fault with the aircraft.

The Safety Window period shown in the diagram almost certainly generates the highest pilot workload, and is regarded as the most critical portion of flight. The overall skills of the pilot are under pressure more at this time than at any other. Altitude changes, aircraft configuration, checklists, communication with air traffic control and instrument interpretation are all sandwiched together inside the Safety Window; and we can extend this one stage further, and overlay the Safety Window concept on any other part of a flight defining a critical period of time.

There is one other important aspect of our original Safety Window we would be wise to consider. Should the pilot leave the window when something goes wrong, or should he stay and land as soon as possible? How do we arrive at such a decision? Consider the case of a twin-jet aircraft in the final phase of an IFR approach and cleared to land. Suddenly there is an engine fire warning, but the crew see no abnormalities with any engine instruments. The captain elects to continue to land the aircraft before dealing with the fire warning, rather than initiate a go-around. This is obviously the right decision and no one would dispute that. In this instance, the best option is to remain in the Safety Window.

Now let's take another scenario for the same aircraft, again in-bound on final approach, and the co-pilot selects gear down and nothing happens. Should the captain continue to hope they can get the gear down at the last

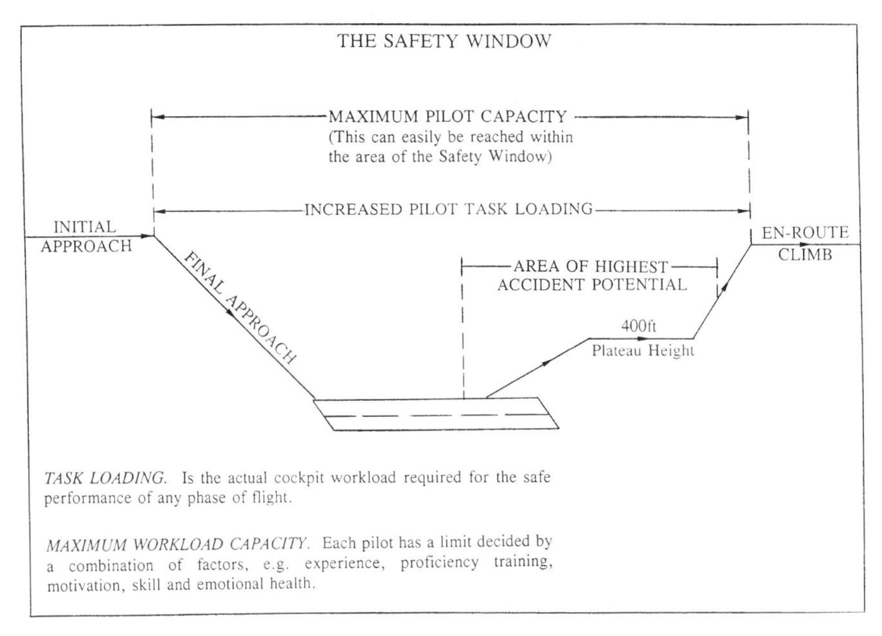

Figure 4

moment and land? Of course there is that possibility, but in an IFR environment at a period of highest workload and stress, one or other of the pilots could miss a vital item and unnecessarily compound the initial problem. The captain informs ATC and initiates the missed approach procedure and is directed to a holding fix outside the Safety Window to sort out the problem. In this case it is clear that leaving the window was the best choice. I know because the incident happened to me and it took several minutes to sort out the problem, therefore that action was the best and safest solution.

Cockpit management summary

Definition The use and co-ordination of all resources available to the crew, so they can achieve the established goal of safety, efficiency and comfort of flight. (N.B. This definition does not exclude resources outside the cockpit.)

General The skills that contribute to good cockpit management can be taught and improved with practice. They are practical skills that are used in day-to-day flight operations.

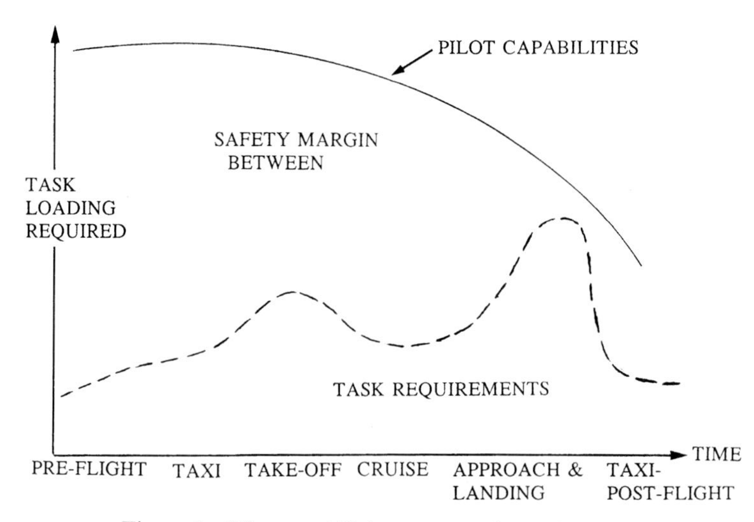

Figure 5 Pilot capabilities versus task requirements

Cockpit management resources For a pilot to be able to use a resource he/she must be aware it exists, and know how to make the best use of it. Being able to identify and utilise all the available resources is essential to the safety of flight.

Communicating skills Effective communication is vitally important between pilots and other aircrew. (N.B. Learning how to listen to other crew members effectively is as important as making sure your information is understood.)

Flight planning and monitoring flight progress This means establishing the parameters and limitations for a flight. It also involves making *progressive* decisions, then taking necessary actions to remain inside the set parameters. This will involve monitoring changing conditions that may affect the parameters and being flexible enough to re-evaluate and establish new limitations as required.

Judgement and decision-making We need to learn the elements of making good decisions and putting them into practice. Making a decision should follow a *logical sequence* in order to collect adequate facts, assess any alternatives, then implement without delay.

Managing people Dealing with people in a manner that will stimulate them into giving their maximum performance for any given set of circumstances.

Using basic (common sense) human psychology as to what makes people tick and how to motivate them. This requires consideration of an individual's personality and level of (aviation) understanding. Being as diplomatic as possible to minimise the risk of verbal confrontation. (It is important to bear in mind that there is always some level of stress in any day-to-day aviation activity.)

Cockpit distractions Every pilot should be able to recognise the sources of distraction in the cockpit, and be able to manage them so they will not interfere with task performance. The consequences of mismanaged distractions have led to major accidents.

Pattern recognition It is very important for all aircrew to recognise chain events that can lead to mistakes and undesirable situations developing. Patterns of events often repeat themselves in one form or another, and if analysed correctly, can be a valuable addition to overall experience. This can also be applied in the recognition of unusual and/or incorrect behaviour in aircrew where it can affect performance and lead to accidents. Research has indicated that people (as well as aircrew) can be taught to recognise and interrupt 'error chains' that might easily result in a serious incident.

Time management and assessment of workload These factors relate to the establishment of priorities (good cockpit management) and the assignment of tasks (which make up the maximum workload in any given period of time. Cockpit tasks have to be organised so they can be completed within the time available.

Chapter 5
Management of Flight Resources

Practical cockpit management skills include flight resource management. This is the effective use of all available people, information, equipment and consumables that will help successfully and safely to complete a flight. They can be either internal or external to the aircraft. The types and availability of flight resources vary widely and are dependent on factors such as aircraft type and equipment, composition of crew, operating environment and geographical location. All pilots should be familiar with as many types of resources as possible, as this will give a pilot greater influence over the progress of a flight. This in turn can greatly increase situational awareness.

Each pilot has a maximum workload capacity, which is influenced by many factors. These include overall experience, specific training and proficiency level. Then there is the important inter-relationship of motivation and emotional health (marriage, financial pressures, job-related stress, promotion/career prospects, illness, etc.). A pilot's maximum workload capacity can therefore vary from day to day and flight to flight, even during a particular flight, if influenced by any combination of factors already mentioned.

Task loading

Task loading is the actual cockpit workload required for the safe performance of any phase of flight. We know there is an average pilot task loading, but sometimes this increases sharply and the pilot has to cope with this for the successful completion of the flight. The causes include abnormal or emergency situations, aircraft equipment and adverse weather problems, high-density air traffic, plus company pressures.

Regardless of any particular flight phase, it is always possible to overload a pilot. Once this happens an accident potential exists and an adequate safety margin must be restored. This can only happen if *all* the available flight resources are utilised effectively. It might merely require a simple reallocation of duties between two pilots to deal with a one-off abnormal task load. However, a pilot who effectively manages flight resources from the beginning of a flight has greater control over cockpit workload. In this case, task loading is less likely to exceed the pilot's capacity to perform safely.

Proper pre-flight planning and conformity to predetermined targets helps to establish and maintain high levels of situational awareness.High levels of situational awareness allow a pilot to operate at peak capacity while keeping task loading under control.

There are four major categories of flight resources:

- human
- operational
- equipment
- consumable

Human resources

Human resources relate to those people who use their individual skills to provide valuable support and are the most varied and variable resources available to a pilot. There are three main headings:

Technical Specialist knowledge and ability, and the aptitude to use it productively.

Inter-personal Interactions between people. The ability to manage others and communicate in ways they understand.

Conceptual The analysis and integration of all associated activities towards a common objective; in aviation, viewing the flight as a whole, and seeing how various phases fit in in relation to the entire profile. These skills include the ability to project, analyse and alter the flight profile accordingly to ensure a successful outcome.

Human resources is the most complex of the categories and can be broken down as follows:

- Flightcrew
- Ground services
- Flight services

FLIGHTCREW

The most important flightcrew resource is oneself. In facing almost any situation or problem, individuals draw upon their own personal skills before turning anywhere else for assistance. A pilot can draw upon his own actual flying skill, level of training and proficiency. Reaching into one's total experience file of knowledge is an excellent way of recognising pattern development. It gives a pilot the ability to make accurate observations, judgements and decisions. Personal resources are therefore the sum total of a pilot's technical, inter-personal and conceptual skills.

GROUND SERVICES

Ground services provide support from pre-flight to post-flight. They are normally only thought of as giving fuel and servicing facilities, but in fact there is far more to it than that. We can include in these services meteorologists, engineers, operations personnel, fixed base operators and manufacturers' representatives. These individuals provide a wealth of valuable services and information that is readily available, either personally or through modern communications facilities. They support the crew and ease the task loading in the cockpit.

FLIGHT SERVICES

Air traffic control facilities in the widest sense. They are the major providers or flight services, and the fastest means of giving routine or emergency assistance to pilots. The range of ATC services includes flight planning, weather briefings, airport traffic control, radar sequencing and en route airways control, crash and rescue services. Additional flight services can also be given by the pilots of other aircraft through the relay of operational messages and weather information.

Operational information

Operational information is a wide range of data that provides the pilot with information needed for planning and decision-making. These include national and international aeronautical information publications and regulations, operations and flight manuals, technical handbooks, performance, en route and instrument let-down charts. Some of this information will be carried in the aircraft for easy reference. Other operational information will be collected as part of pre-flight preparation, such as weather briefs, flight plans (ATC and navigational), NOTAMS, aircraft load sheets (weight and balance computations) and passenger manifests. To be effective, operational information must be current, readily available, and applicable to a particular flight and the planned route. Anything which has expired or is obsolete can only lead to poor planning and decision-making, and could become critical to the safety of the flight.

Equipment

To help the pilot operate in a more complex environment, sophisticated equipment has been developed. We can categorise equipment resources as:

- Communications equipment
- Status indicators

- Predictors
- Labour-saving devices

Like all flight resources, these various categories of equipment overlap and support one another. Either individually or collectively, equipment resources help pilots achieve and maintain high levels of situational awareness.

Communications equipment

Communications equipment facilitates the transfer of information to and from the cockpit. VHF and HF radios, flight phones and transponders connect a pilot with many valuable sources of support. They form an integrated network, providing an up-to-the-second, highly reliable information collecting, processing and disseminating capability. Radio communications link a pilot with many of the human resources that are available. In addition to receiving instructions and guidance, a pilot can make intentions and needs known to those capable of providing services and support.

Status indicators

Status indicators are basic building blocks for achieving and maintaining high levels of situational awareness. They provide valuable information on the current status of the aircraft, and enhance planning and decision-making. Some examples of status indicators include weather radar, radar, navigational equipment, flight instruments, systems indicators, annunciator lights and audible warnings.

Predictors

Predictors allow pilots to accurately estimate future needs and plan accordingly. Time-to-station read-outs, fuel management and flight planning computers, inertial navigation systems, GPS and associated equipment provide timely indications of potential problems, thereby allowing sufficient time for corrective action. Other examples of predictors include stall warning and ground proximity warning systems, and windshear alerts.

Labour-saving devices

Labour-saving devices reduce pilot workload by providing load sharing. Trends in aircraft development are towards consolidated flight management and the delegation of routine tasks to automated systems. The benefit of this is to increase situational awareness when a pilot is relieved of many routine cockpit duties. What we must understand is that these sophisticated systems cannot be responsible for the safety of the flight – that remains the sole responsibility of the pilot-in-command.

Consumable resources

Consumable resources are those resources used during the course of the flight. Because they are consumable, they impose limits on a flight. The most important three of these resources are fuel, personal energy and time. Efficient management of each one is critical to flight. The key to the effective use of a consumable resource is careful planning on the following lines:

- How much is required?
- How much is available?
- How can it be used efficiently?
- How can we ensure sufficient reserves are available?

Personal energy is a consumable resource. Energy fuels the body in the same way an aircraft requires fuel. Not enough attention is given to building up and conserving this resource. Proper rest, nutrition, and utilising relaxation techniques all go towards maintaining good physical condition and high personal energy levels. This will of course help to boost individual situational awareness.

Establishing realistic targets and practising time management throughout a flight will help pilots avoid time-related losses and manage other consumable resources more effectively. Time lost can never be regained. Time management and integration of flight resources is a skill every pilot should develop and refine. We have seen that there is an abundance of flight resources available to a pilot. The effective flight resource manager will take the initiative to learn what they are, where they can be found, and how to use them effectively.

Cockpit management essentials

We have looked at many aspects of practical cockpit management, but what about cockpit safety? This requires the application of six skills:

- asking the right questions
- stating opinions frankly
- working out differences
- criticising in a constructive manner
- making decisions
- managing resources effectively

In addition, there are six rules for safe operation within the cockpit:

- the positive delegation of flying and monitoring responsibilities must be a top priority
- the positive delegation of monitoring responsibilities is just as important as the positive delegation of flying responsibilities

- the pilot flying the aircraft should avoid performing secondary tasks, unless absolutely operationally essential
- whenever there are conflicting interpretations of fact, external sources of information must be used to resolve the problem
- whenever there is conflicting information from two sources, cross-checking from an independent source is necessary
- if any crew member has a doubt about a clearance, procedure or situation, he or she must make that doubt known to other crew members

Checklists: why have them?

All of us at one time or another have heard a long list of excuses for not using checklists: 'Checklists take too much time', or 'I know my aircraft so well, I don't need the checklist any more'; the list is endless. But the one that really stands out in my mind is, 'I fly a simple aircraft, I don't need a checklist!' In my view, this is the most misguided one of all. It may well be true that there are fewer items to remember when flying less sophisticated aircraft. However, it is also true that simple aircraft don't always have simple procedures, or simple systems. It is just as easy to forget a simple action as it is to forget a more complex one, particularly in times of stress and a high cockpit workload when your attention is divided.

I have regularly come across pilots who have taken off with pitot-static covers and static plugs still in place, cargo doors not latched properly and many other items. This might well lead only to an aborted take-off and some embarrassed, red-faced pilots, but it could also result in a major accident. Each year, many aviation incidents and notifiable accidents are caused by failure to use the checklist. One typical extract from an official investigation report read: 'The pre-flight was not conducted in accordance with the aircraft approved checklist, and was a major factor in the resulting accident.'

If you follow the checklist conscientiously each and every time it is required, you are a professional. Deviate from this and you are risking your life. The other important point we can draw from this is, if checklist discipline is lacking, then discipline may be lacking in other areas as well. After all, discipline is a prime factor in reaching and maintaining a high level of competence and professionalism in flying. FAA regulations require that a cockpit checklist be used during operations under Parts 91, 121 and 135. Certainly all the various civil aviation authorities I have dealt with around the world require an approved checklist to be used in all professional operations. As we can see, they are an important ingredient of good cockpit management and therefore contribute to a high level of situational awareness.

Captain Starlight: 'How can I be expected to turn 15 pages of a Boeing 737-400 checklist into a *useable mnemonic*? As it is my copilot, Marcus Dumbell, has difficulty understanding some of the "technical" phrases in PLAYBOY magazine!'

Definition and purpose of a checklist

A checklist is an essential tool used to initiate, direct and progress essential operational activities in the cockpit. It establishes a common method of communication between flightcrew and serves as a written aid in accomplishing essential crew activities. The checklist, therefore, helps ensure that the crew is prepared, and has configured the aircraft and its systems for the related phase of the flight. It is not to be regarded as a substitute for a thorough knowledge of the aircraft systems and procedures. This final point can never be overstated or repeated too often.

Checklist design

Having trained pilots of many nationalities around the world on various aircraft types, I know that the checklist is the one item that causes the most arguments. Each cockpit leads itself to a logical 'flow pattern'. This helps the pilots complete all the procedures and configure the aircraft. The design of the checklist should take this into account. For example, the flow may be from left to right or top to bottom. But where possible, all actions or cross-checks should be completed on a specific systems panel, or area, before moving on to the next. It gives the checklist a logical progression and cuts out unnecessary further checks in areas already covered. Fewer errors or omissions are the result, as well as faster completion of the checklist.

It is the Normal Procedures checklist I have found causes the most problems. Although these are the most routine, accident and incident investigations highlight that missed normal checklist items often contribute to gear-up landings, fuel-starved engines, incorrect flap or trim settings, and crew-induced malfunctions. The part that really causes confusion is the actual content, the items that should or should not be included in the checklist, and where. The manufacturer says one thing, the training organisation may state another, so the operator then faces a dilemma and has to find a workable operational solution. In the end, though, it is the operator who must decide what works most efficiently.

The best way is for the operator to work with the manufacturer's Technical Field Support Department, which always includes very experienced training pilots. This will provide the operator with the best available information in solving checklist problems. In my book, the worst kind of pilot is the one who performs his or her own 'surgery' to the established checklist, thinking his or her version saves time and gets the job done just as well. No prizes for guessing what can happen as a result.

Checklists have evolved over many years and have been organised into categories and sub-categories. These have proved to be the most effective way to carry out desired procedures. They include Normal, Emergency and Abnormal checklists.

Emergency Checklists

These are used to isolate and compensate for failed or malfunctioning systems to protect the aircraft from immediate or critical harm. For instance, an engine or electrical fire would be associated with the emergency checklist.

The checklist should be limited to the minimum number of items considered to be essential to aid the pilot in an emergency, and in concise, abbreviated form, designed to remind pilots of items to check without providing details concerning the operation of any one system. In precise terms there will be:

- Immediate or Initial Actions (memory items) checklist, when sequence is essential to safety
- Subsequent Actions (challenge and response) read items for two-pilot

operation, or by 'Item' and 'Condition' headings for single-pilot aircraft. For example:

CHALLENGE OR ITEM	RESPONSE OR CONDITION
GENERATOR	CROSS-COUPLE

This is to provide pilots with a better understanding of the reasons behind their immediate actions. Completion of this is designed to contain the emergency and isolate the malfunctioning system.

Abnormal Checklists

Give procedures for non-standard conditions that do not represent an *immediate* threat to the safety of the aircraft or its occupants. Failure of one part of an electrical, navigation or communications system would fall into the category.

Well-designed checklists contain:

- only those items necessary to accomplish the task or resolve the problem
- items listed in the correct order
- arrangements that do not interfere with the flying of the aircraft

Therefore, we can see that checklists are constructed to assist, not hinder, operations. However, the use of checklists does not necessarily mean that items won't be missed, but there are established techniques that will help prevent this happening. The main point to remember is the importance of using checklists in exactly the same sequence and pattern. Doing it this way makes it more likely to detect missed items or deviations.

Finally, a word of warning. Any checklist is only as good as the flight crew member using it. Disciplined self-motivation when going through each item will ensure nothing is missed. The answer is to gather the maximum concentration of mind and body in the process of using the checklist. Familiarity and inattention, called 'Checklist Lassitude', is the greatest enemy.

Challenge and response technique

One proven and effective way of running a checklist is the challenge and response to technique. It has been used for many years by professional pilots to ensure accuracy and good communication for normal, abnormal and emergency checklists. One pilot initiates each checklist item verbally, stating exactly what is written, i.e. the challenge. A second pilot responsible for performing the item responds accordingly. A sample extract from a two-pilot checklist is given below:

AFTER ENGINE START CHECKLIST			READ	ANSWER
1	Start Master	Normal	RP	LP
2	Ignition L & R	Off	RP	LP
3	Electrical Master	Internal	RP	LP
4	Generators	On	RP	LP
5	Volts & Amps	Checked	RP	LP
6	Shedding Bus R & L	Normal	RP	LP
7	External Supply	Disconnected	RP	LP
8	All MIs	Check vertical	RP	LP
9	Fuel Levelling Valves	Shut/MI vertical	RP	LP
10	Flaps	Set & Check	RP	LP
11	Warning Lights	Standard Three	RP	LP/RP
12	Engine Instruments	Checked	RP	LP/RP
13	Air Conditioning	As Required	RP	RP
14	Emergency Brakes	Normal	RP	LP
15	Parking Brakes	Off	RP	LP
16	Toe Brakes	Exercise	RP	LP
17	Parking Brakes	Set	RP	LP
18	Cabin Clear	Received	RP	LP
19	Wheel Chocks	Removed	RP	LP
20	Taxi Clearance	Received	RP	RP
21	Parking Brakes	Off	RP	LP
22	Taxi Light	On	RP	RP
			Checklist Complete	

This system has proved effective whether two pilots are involved, or one pilot issues both the challenge and the response.

A useful way to improve the effectiveness of challenge and response is to Say, Look and Touch.

Saying each item out loud stimulates the sense of hearing and helps focus attention. From this, a pilot can monitor his own actions and prevent confusion and distraction in high-stress situations.

Looking helps ensure that variation between the checklist instruction and the control position or instrument reading will show up immediately.

Touching involves the third 'doing' sense. The physical act of the pilot touching the item, whether operating or checking it, completes the focus of attention.

Using the challenge and response method is useful in countering stress, fatigue, divided attention and the old enemy, complacency.

Pacing the checklist

Using the checklist to the best advantage can be accomplished by proper pacing: completing appropriate checklists as soon as possible to avoid interference caused by high density traffic, bad weather, minor aircraft technical problems and stress; not letting attention-dividing situations put you behind the aircraft.

Pacing is extremely important when using Abnormal and Emergency checklists. Going through a critical checklist too fast can have very serious consequences. There are many recorded instances where perfectly good engines have been shut down by rushing into the emergency checklist before the real problem was identified. Only few emergencies require *immediate* action. The first and primary objective when faced with an emergency situation is to fly and control the aircraft. Then you can safely identify the problem, perform any memory items and use the appropriate emergency checklist methodically and accurately.

The points already made here apply equally well to single-pilot operations. An effective self-challenge and response technique is very helpful to ensure all checklist items are covered. In fact, whether you are flying single or multiple crew, if you talk to yourself and begin hearing answers, then you have learned well; you are not going crazy!

Limitations to checklists

One important point that should be clearly understood is well worth restating. The checklist is not a substitute for knowledge, or I should say lack of knowledge of systems, aircraft performance and operating conditions. Without the knowledge, even the meticulous use of the checklist can lead to a great many problems. A technical malfunction may be incorrectly identified and the wrong checklist used to deal with it. This might easily compound the problems and make the emergency much worse, and could easily lead to serious consequences that would endanger the safety of the aircraft. Obviously there is not a checklist for every imaginable problem that might occur. Checklists do not fly the aircraft.

Summary

- checklists assist in checking or verifying that the aircraft and equipment are in the correct configuration
- they initiate and direct communication and related activities

- checklists provide a list of items or procedures designed to guard against failures of the human memory, particularly in times of stress and divided attention

The concepts outlined here apply regardless of size or technical complexity of the aircraft, type of checklist used, or the composition of the flightcrew. We *can* train to be safe, and we *can* develop both our cockpit management skills and situational awareness. But no matter what the situation, the best safety device in any aircraft is a well-trained crew. Safety does not just happen – you make it happen.

Chapter 6
Making CRM Work

A pilot's flying experience will not change the basic essentials of crew resource/safety management. Every flight always requires good resource management and sound co-operation between all crew members on the flight deck. This means an effective balancing of pilot skills, good interaction between the crew, and an intelligent use of communications together with an overall high level of situational awareness.

Having made these important points, let's look at a typical General Aviation scenario and see what can happen.

Low-time but knowledge sharp

Andy Beaumont was a relatively low-time commercial pilot who had used the 'self-improver' route to gain his professional qualifications. Two years as a flight instructor on low pay, investing every penny he could afford to gain better qualifications, meant he had little to spend on anything else. So when he drove his battered old VW into the staff car park at the London Luton Airport FBO, he parked it out of the way in a far corner against the perimeter fence. He was suddenly embarrassed by its appearance. This was his first flight for Wright Engineering as a corporate pilot, and he was anxious that nothing would stand in the way of a good first impression. Therefore, he had arrived very early for the flight. Now that his salary was double his previous instructor pay he could afford a more presentable car.

Andy felt it was the most important day of his professional pilot career to date. He had moved up from flight instructor and occasional charter pilot to a brand new position as corporate pilot flying an executive jet. The Cessna Citation he was to fly was the highlight of his career to that moment. He had completed his co-pilot training without any problems and was now eager to start flying. Andy looked upon his new position as much more than a job. It was a golden opportunity to take a major step forward in his flying career.

Captain Darren Rhodes, his chief pilot, was busy on the phone when Andy entered the cramped office the company rented as their Ops room. Andy had known Darren for over five years and respected him as an experienced pilot. In fact he was old enough to be Andy's father. Darren's main problem was 'people management', and he found the responsibility of running the small flight department quite stressful. What had compounded his problems was the fact that he had lost two previous co-pilots to airlines in fewer than eighteen months. This had built up additional frustrations when it came to stabilising the whole corporate operation. Added to that, his wife had just been admitted to hospital for a major operation.

At that moment, Darren was speaking with one of the company directors who planned to be a passenger on that day's flight. Inevitably, there were last-minute changes to the flight schedule timings with a new destination. In his mind, Darren's *perception* of Andy's experience led him to believe that re-flight planning the Citation schedule was beyond him, especially on his first day with the company. He was already under some (self-imposed) personal stress, and felt it would be better to cope with the situation himself.

When Darren saw Andy, a look of relief crossed his face. He clamped his hand over the mouthpiece of the telephone. 'Thank goodness you're here, we've got an earlier departure, so take care of the pre-flight and I'll be out in a few minutes. Brief you later.' Within ten minutes both men were strapped into their respective seats in the Citation's cockpit. The checklist had the effect of concentrating both their minds, blocking out other problems. It was an empty 'positioning' flight to Manchester to pick up two company directors, together with a client who was visiting from the Far East. Then it was direct to Frankfurt in Germany with the minimum delay. Darren wanted to make a good impression.

Rather belatedly, after they were already taxiing, Darren said, 'I filed airways and flow control said we shouldn't have any landing delays. I want to avoid refuelling as that would really make us late.'

In spite of the rushed departure, Andy had managed to have a brief look at the met information for the route. 'Looks like we've got some heavy thunderstorm activity on our route, otherwise the TAFS look reasonably good for our destination and alternates.'

Darren hardly acknowledged the remark, simply saying, 'Let's make sure we get to Manchester as fast as possible, we don't want to keep the passengers waiting. I'll fly this leg so you can see how it goes.'

The take-off and climb to a low *en route* cruising altitude for the thirty-minute flight was routine. Andy had to work hard to keep up with the speed at which things were happening – radio call, setting and resetting radio and navaid frequencies, as well as handling a pressurisation system, an unfamiliar experience to him. As it turned out, ATC directed them into a holding pattern for fifteen minutes before being cleared for the final approach. A thirty-minute flight had turned into a frustrating one hour.

When the Citation reached the allotted parking bay, Andy saw the chief pilot was agitated. So when he queried whether he should ask their handling agent for fuel, he was told curtly, 'They had enough to get them to Frankfurt, no problem.' Being inexperienced on type, and feeling somewhat tentative on his first day with the company, Andy did not dispute the decision, he merely busied himself with preparations for the onward flight to Frankfurt.

The chief pilot left the aircraft with the handling agent and went into the main terminal to greet the passenger, something he would not normally do if he was late. But that day he considered it as a VIP flight.

By the time they were airborne again, they were one hour and thirty minutes behind schedule, with further delays on start-up and while taxiing. The passengers were seasoned corporate air travellers and helped themselves to the coffee and sandwiches provided. This left Andy free to concentrate on his new and unfamiliar co-pilot duties.

As they progressed towards Frankfurt in clear skies, Darren suddenly realised they hadn't switched on the radar. Immediately he did, the screen began to show a clear return from a solid line of storms near the two-hundred-mile scale. When Andy changed to the next VHF frequency (a Frankfurt area controller), there were many calls from pilots requesting deviations of heading around some bad storm cells. At one hundred miles the storms were clearly visible, with several of the Cb build-ups reported as rising to over 50,000 feet. Already several aircraft in-bound to Frankfurt were holding due to an extensive and violent thunderstorm immediately over the airport.

'There's going to be some pretty severe turbulence in that lot,' Andy remarked, looking ahead at the build-ups. 'Do we have enough fuel to hold, then get to Stuttgart if necessary?"

Darren glanced at the radar screen and said, 'Let's press on and look for a way through.' He knew the delays had eaten into their fuel reserves, and it would be tight if they had to divert. He now regretted not having refuelled at Manchester.

Inside, Andy felt uneasy, his aviation 'sixth sense' warning him all was not as it should be. Professionalism overcame his reserve. 'I'll check the Stuttgart weather if you like,' Andy offered.

Darren merely shrugged, saying, 'Okay,' his attention focused on other things.

The Citation continued on course until they could see the build-ups were a solid, continuous line with no visible breaks. Now the storms were directly ahead, crossing the twenty-five-mile scale, with still no break in the line.

Thirty seconds later, the radar screen suddenly went blank. The circuit breaker had tripped.

'Okay, I'll get it,' Darren stated. 'It's happened before but no one can isolate the problem.' Darren moved in his seat and bent down below the level of the instrument panel, then struggled to reset the circuit breaker.

By this time, the aircraft was encountering moderate turbulence from the outer edges of the thunderstorms that were now only about fifteen miles ahead. Andy felt unsure of his captain's intentions as the radar was dead. He knew he was anxious to find a way through rather than compromise their fuel situation any further with a detour, which would further delay their arrival. Andy apprehensively watched the heavy Cbs getting closer as Darren fumbled awkwardly to reset the breaker.

By the time the colour radar screen lit up again, the Citation was very close to the first thunderstorm, with lightning flashing from cloud to cloud and continuous turbulence. Darren looked up and suddenly appeared both annoyed and tense that they were so dangerously close to the storm. He used the autopilot to turn northwards away from the Cbs. 'Tell Frankfurt what we're doing – and by the way, I hope you were not going to let us fly into that muck?'

Trying not to show how uncomfortable he felt, Andy busied himself on the radio while Darren used the radar and his eyes to try to find a break in the line of storms. The weather diversion took almost twenty-five minutes before they were able to turn direct for Frankfurt and obtain descent clearance.

Andy turned to his chief pilot. 'I wasn't sure what you wanted to do back there – about altering course, I mean.'

'With me trying to sort out the radar problem I assumed you would be flying the aircraft. It was one of the points I wanted to cover in the briefing we missed this morning.'

While Andy sorted out the IFR approach charts, Darren continued the descent. The thunderstorm had cleared through by the time they were being radar-vectored for runway 25 at Frankfurt. The weather was broken Strato-Cu between 2,000 and 5,000 feet.

'ATC probably won't advise us whether it will be 25L or 25R (being parallel runways) until the last minute,' said Darren, 'so set up 25L on my side and 25R on yours, then you can alter the redundant frequency when we know.'

Approach Control advised them it would be runway 25R and continued radar vectors for the ILS. Andy became so absorbed with the radio and Darren with the flying (he was now flying the Citation manually) that Andy forgot to reset the No. 1 (captain's) ILS. When the Citation was established on the ILS localiser and glidescope at 2,500 feet, approach radar queried if they were on the localiser for 25R – then reminded them of the correct frequency. Andy realised immediately he had not reset the frequency, with Darren failing to cross-check. Fortunately at that moment they broke out of cloud and were able to manoeuvre visually for 25R. Had it not been for the alertness and professional discretion of a radar controller, there could have been a serious incident.

Andy was very relieved when they landed safely and shut down on the ramp in the General Aviation parking area. It was only then he realised how tired and emotionally drained he felt. He could also see from the fuel remaining that they would have been hard-pressed to reach their alternate if that had been necessary. Leaving Andy to look after the post-flight duties and liaise with the handling agent, Darren accompanied the passengers. He told Andy he would catch up with him later at their hotel.

Management essentials

Even in the larger commercial airlines, most pre-flight as well as in-flight situations are influenced by a variety of personal styles. The incidents related in the corporate aviation flight described here actually happened.

Studying and analysing the entire flight, including the events preceding it, will help to concentrate your thoughts about CRM, in particular on the principles of safety management. Think about what you would have done in the circumstances, because as individual pilots we all react to aviation pressures differently. Afterwards, carry the solutions to these problems into your everyday flying operations.

Management essentials are therefore all about managing resources and making decisions about making the best use of them.

As we saw from our scenario, corporate flying can be a minefield of problems involving operations, the various stressors and the delicate balance of inter-relationships between crew and the needs of passengers. Here we have a classic situation of experienced older captain and novice (to the corporate operation) low-time co-pilot. Darren Rhodes obviously contributed far more experience and proficiency to the flight than Andy Beaumont, his new co-pilot. However, Andy had good background experience as an instructor. This would have provided valuable resources to the occasion, in spite of his brand new co-pilot status with the company. Unfortunately, Darren appeared to disregard Andy's potential, and missed the opportunity of better controlling the operational stress he was under in tackling the pre-flight problems which had been thrust upon him.

The storyline also reveals two areas that are in direct opposition to skills which ensure good cockpit management: asking the right questions; and frankly stating opinions. Darren failed to ask questions, let alone the right ones. Andy was too anxious to make a good impression on the first day in his new job, and seeing Darren's stressed attitude, felt it was inappropriate to offer a frank opinion. Quite naturally, he was also a little nervous. Andy could have made a meaningful contribution to the overall conduct of the flight because he had many assets. But his abilities were wasted from the start. Darren had lost sight of the fact that although Andy was new to corporate flying, he was a *professional*, and could certainly have coped with re-planning the flight, thus taking some of the last-minute workload off his shoulders.

The very fact that Andy was new should have been sufficient reason to draw him into the planning process if only as a form of familiarisation and company training. Darren also missed another good training opportunity for Andy when he decided to fly the Citation on the empty positioning leg from Luton to Manchester. Caught up in the rush of an earlier departure, Darren could still have taken the opportunity of briefing Andy as he had said he would, immediately before start-up at Luton. He did not think the situation through and ignored the role of his co-pilot.

It is unfortunately a flaw of many managers. They have no difficulty making decisions, but often base those decisions on either incomplete information or lack of thought. The chief pilot took an avoidable risk by not refuelling at Manchester, particularly in view of the fact that there were known departure delays. Then, on the flight to Frankfurt, Darren failed to use several resources. The first was his co-pilot. It must be remembered that the positive delegation of monitoring responsibilities is just as important as the positive delegation of flying duties. The radar was left off until it was needed. You might consider this as minor, but it is one more instance of a failure to ask the right questions. Another important resource that was not utilised was the Air Traffic Control radar system. It could have provided information about clear routes between or round the edge of the extensive line of thunderstorms. But that information was never requested. Darren had the ideal opportunity when Andy suggested obtaining the latest weather for Stuttgart, their flight-planned alternate. Again it was a failure to use the resources available from his new co-pilot.

With Darren continuing to fly the aircraft, he was not really giving Andy adequate instruction. Instead, he chose to fly the aircraft, navigate, make fuel calculations and work the radar. He was also looking outside the cockpit to try to find a hole in the bad weather. Andy was reduced to basic radio communications and secondary observation. When the radar went off, he immediately struggled about in the cockpit to sort it out, leaving Andy as a mere onlooker with no clear instructions for what he should be doing. When the aircraft almost flew into a massive Cb, Darren blamed Andy, either ignoring or forgetting the fact he had not given him any guidance as to the immediate conduct of the flight while he fixed the radar fault. Andy could have – and should have – asked what Darren wanted him to do, being involved in a cockpit distraction, but he didn't. The opportunity for communication is a two-way street.

By ignoring the positive delegation of cockpit responsibilities, the cockpit management was poor throughout the flight, particularly with the lack of instruction from Darren in setting the ILS for the final approach into Frankfurt. Had it not been for the alertness and discretion of the approach-radar controller, there could have been a nasty incident. The assignment of support responsibilities within the cockpit, regardless of to whom these responsibilities are assigned, is just as important as the workload division, which is vital to safety.

Many airlines and multi-crew operations use the terms Flying Pilot (FP) and Non-Flying Pilot (NFP) to differentiate between the primary and support role. It is a regular occurrence for the captain to be the NFP. These two designations of course refer to the immediate flying responsibilities, rather than the legal chain of command. Nevertheless, the distinction between the two responsibilities is valuable to know, being in wide general use.

In some ways it is understandable that Andy failed to observe another important cockpit rule: if any crew member has a doubt about a clearance, procedure or situation, he or she must make that doubt known to other crew members. Andy's new co-pilot status in a small corporate operation, and the situation he faced, created a double problem for him. He had a doubt about the situation, and did not make that doubt known to his supervising crew member, the chief pilot. Good cockpit management is always dependent on a joint effort. Andy was certainly professional enough to see and know that Darren was not exercising the right command authority, so he should have made a greater effort to compensate, diplomatically and respectfully, by asking the right questions. He only approached the question of weather in a rather oblique way. He should have stated his opinion and obtained a resolution.

In fact, both pilots missed the opportunity for a constructive critique on the events that had taken place during the flight. A frank discussion on how to improve the inter-personal crew co-operation, thus minimising or avoiding future problems, would have been beneficial to both men. It was Darren's place to provide the guidance for his new co-pilot, certainly very necessary at the beginning of a close professional working relationship.

Leaving Andy very much to his own devices by going off with the passengers, Darren missed a golden opportunity for a quiet post-flight debrief, particularly after failing to give him pre-flight instructions on the conduct of the flight. The chief pilot could only have imagined what his new co-pilot was thinking, and thus he was likely to come to some wrong and perhaps prejudicial conclusions. On the other hand, Andy could have cleared the air and learned something about his chief pilot's personal style and priorities. Unfortunately, human nature being what it is, avoiding unpleasant subjects is always easier. As we know from our own jobs, *constructive* criticism and discussion can be a psychologically demanding affair.

What are your conclusions?

Well, regardless of whether you are more often the flying pilot, or the non-flying pilot, your personal analysis about how the situation (the conduct of the flight) could have been improved is an important part in developing a total awareness of good cockpit safety and resource management. It is therefore your considered personal conclusion that will improve the cockpit relationship that you must maintain. When you have thought about it and have listed the best solutions to the corporate flight scenario, do not forget about them on your next flight.

Summary

- a pilot's flying experience will not change the essentials of cockpit safety and resource management
- we need to develop the effective balance of piloting, communications, crew interaction, leadership and managing all the available resources

Safe operation within the cockpit:

- needs positive delegation of flying and monitoring duties (FP and NFP) – this is a top priority
- conflicting information from two sources should always be cross-checked from an independent source
- with conflicting interpretations of fact, external sources of information must be used to resolve the conflict
- the Flying Pilot (FP) should avoid performing secondary tasks unless absolutely necessary, as it is an unwanted cockpit distraction
- any doubt in the cockpit should be resolved immediately by communication

Skills to be developed

- asking the *right* questions and *frankly* stating opinions in the interests of safety
- constructive criticism to work out differences
- avoid any delay in making decisions
- know as much as possible about the range of different resources available, and use them in the most effective manner.

CHAPTER 7

A GUIDE TO THE ISSUES AND RESPONSIBILITIES THAT AFFECT MANAGEMENT PILOTS

The implications of CRM training for management

First of all, let us consider a cross-section of the key messages in Crew Resource Management training (both explicit and implicit) that aircrew would be expected to have after a course:

- consultation improves the quality of the final decision
- non-technical training is an essential part of the training syllabus as a whole
- authoritarianism is destructive
- teamwork is essential
- awareness of others is important
- people are not perfect
- no one can work in isolation

The number one question that then arises is whether flight management can relate these principles to their own attitudes and behaviour as managers. The general consensus of opinion is that management tended to fail this test more often than it passed it, although there were widely differing experiences from company to company. We then have to ask if it *matters* whether or not management attitudes and behaviour are consistent with the principles of good CRM. In other words, should we *expect* managers to conduct themselves according to the same moral attitudes that facilitate safety, working effectiveness and general well-being on the flight deck?

What we can say is that CRM is not a substitute or replacement for good overall general management practice, because it does not cover every aspect of management, although having said that CRM-type principles seem to fall into line with accepted management style. However, if we fail to apply them on the flight deck we can soon run into operational difficulties with profound consequences. Similarly, if management ignores the CRM principles its performance will suffer with the obvious knock-on effects.

The problems of human factors training

'For what reason do I need human factors training?' I have heard some pilots say. 'I passed all my flight training, I have my professional pilot's licence and I am proficient, so why do I need anything else?'

What we must understand is that CRM-type attitudes and skills do not come naturally to every aircrew member. Unfortunately they are easy to sabotage. So we must be sensitive to the fragility of the success of human factors training. Flightcrew are trained 'observers' and are able to detect even slight technical problems in their working environment. They carry this skill into other areas of their lives. Therefore, when they see management problems, they want to know *why* when these problems are not properly addressed. Are there two sets of rules, one for the thinking, decision-making management, and another for the practical flight crews?

In general all aircrew have a short 'tolerance fuse' and do not suffer fools gladly, or lack of what *they perceive* as the inability to take essential decisions. After all, in their (flight deck) environment the quick resolution of (technical safety-threatening) problems has to be achieved immediately. For them irresolution produces impatience and often cynicism. Flight managers (mostly practising or ex-senior pilots) regard this type of confrontational problem as a real aggravation to themselves (as management). The crews are not thrilled about it either, regarding it as an unnecessary waste of time.

Then there are the individual Jekyll and Hyde personality flight managers who often compound the problems. Having crossed the fence into management, they start to say and do the opposite of what they did before. I came across a very bad example of this in a well-known overseas airline some years ago. I was the General Manager's Training Captain. He succeeded in causing chaos from the moment he took over his (management) position. A number of pilots made a swift exit, myself among them. But the 'top management', co-opted from a government department, did nothing. The Flight Manager in question simply recruited new pilots! This episode highlights a real problem. After a few enquiries, I discovered that only a small percentage of Flight Managers have actually had real management training. It is not sufficient to have, for example, twenty years as a captain, with perhaps Check and Training (technical) experience, then suddenly to be thrown into the management environment. It can be a daunting experience which many cannot cope with.

The need for management training

Fortunately, many of the larger companies have seen the light and are confronting management training head-on. It is the medium to smaller ones that are not keeping pace, mainly because of financial constraints, but also due to the fact that they think (perceive) they have enough 'management expertise' already, an unwise viewpoint showing a distinct lack of executive foresight brought about by a blinkered, prejudiced outlook.

Few flight managers have been exposed to the range of problems they can encounter in their position. This is due to the lack of induction training and follow-up development to increase their management skills, which managers in other departments have. Flight managers need training in management skills just as intensively as they did when developing operational pilot skills on the flight deck. Therefore, the best and most effective managers have a combination of experience matched by education and training appropriate to their level of responsibility.

Safety as a prerequisite to commercial survival

There is another viewpoint we haven't covered so far, that crew members don't care about management. There are many instances where this is undoubtedly true, but it is certainly contrary to the principle that the whole company's teamwork is essential for harmony, the general 'feel-good' factor and safety – which means survival. Therefore it follows that safety is a prerequisite to commercial survival.

Nevertheless, the responsibility for safety cannot be completely transferred to the flight deck crews. Ensuring the best possible level of safety is not sufficient to 'guarantee' commercial success. There is too much competition in today's aviation industry. Safety and commercial prosperity are an interwoven pattern of (company) organisation and managerial factors that are beyond the daily scope and control of crews. There has to be a large measure of inter-company co-operation between management and flight crews for the maximum benefit to be gained.

So where do we go from here? Flight Managers must be able to cope with the demands that crew training creates: financial, performance-related, involvement in problem-solving, the answers to fuel policy, time-keeping and liaison with cabin crews; then there is ground operations and overseeing ramp handling.

Flight manager as key motivator

The Flight Manager is the one in charge of Crew Resource Management training. If he looks sideways (across the management structure) he can decide how other departments can gain from CRM training, as well as the crews themselves.

Two of the most significant differences that have to be faced involve overcoming perceived status differences, and mistrust of something that is not fully understood and which disturbs the status quo. These issues are not something to be tackled by the faint-hearted or 'yes men'.

There is no tangible way accurately to measure the effects of CRM training, because there is no hi-tech device that can define exactly what is going on inside the human mind. We can only make deductions from observation of attitudes. This makes it difficult to gauge the human variables that might cause threats, not only to safety, but to the commercial well-being of a company as well. Hopefully one of the long-term spin-off benefits to emerge from CRM training will be a better understanding of the role management plays within the company structure. There is no doubt that the best and most successful management is one committed to the right level of investment in flight safety.

Identifying constraints

How much can be achieved will always depend on:

- the company resources available
- the structure of the organisation
- the quality of staff

Remember, a company can only be as good as the quality and level of expertise of the people working for it. Certainly it can only be helpful to make a list of the constraints, as these will identify the barriers to progress. Let's review an extract from a university school of management syllabus, and then compare it with our CRM course. I'm sure you will recognise a number of similar disciplines in this syllabus.

Managing of Information
Managing of the Environment
Decision-Making
Strategic Management
Human Resource Management
Training and Development
Inter-Personal Skills
Health and Safety
Validation and Evaluation of Training

Behavioural Studies
Technology Management
Corporate Strategy
Applied Social Science
Employee Development
Employee Relations
Training and Appraisal
Recruitment and Selection
Training Methods

Knowing and understanding how an integrated company structure works in the long run makes us better managers.

Basic components of any complex productive system

(Fallible decision)	*Decision-makers*	(Corporate Management)
(Deficiencies)	*Line Management*	(Operations, Maintenance, Training)
(No skill, poor equipment)	*Preconditions*	(Reliable equipment, skilled and motivated workforce)
(Unsafe acts)	*Productive Activities* *The Product*	(Integration of human and machine)
(Inadequate)	*Defences* *The Pilot*	(Safeguards against foreseeable hazards)

SOURCE OF INFORMATION: James Reason, *Human Error 1990, UK* Cambridge University Press.

Summary

The main areas that are worth detailed study cover:

- inter-personal skills
- decision-making
- stress management (self-recognition and recognition in others)
- recognising dangerous attitudes in others
- management of change
- morale
- accountability
- performance indicators (skill, CRM effectiveness)
- financial cost-benefit
- regulatory aspects
- legal aspects – being individual and corporate responsibility
- selection of crew
- training and training records
- CRM for Training Captain

CHAPTER 8
SOME FACTS IN RELATION TO ACCIDENTS

Safety must always be a priority

As far as any normal responsible operator is concerned, safety has a very high priority. Safety must also be a state of mind for aviation personnel. This is because an operator's reputation depends on passenger confidence.

We have seen the well-publicised results of repetitive flight delays caused by technical problems on public transport flights. Loss of passenger confidence can easily force an operator out of business. We all know that flight safety costs money, but we cannot ignore it, or worse still, cut corners. Ultimately that is a recipe for disaster.

The effects of accidents

Accidents have an extremely detrimental effect on reputation, and thus productivity. It is impossible to put a price on it. Passengers have a right to safe carriage, and accident prevention is management's responsibility. In 1988, two-thirds of total losses involved airlines known to be under-financed, or owned by countries with economic difficulties (IATA).

IATA safety record for 1992

Accident classification – hull losses; subjective assessments of human factors 1992

Active failure (non-adherence to standard operating procedures)	4
Passive failure (unawareness)	6
Proficiency failure (inappropriate handling of aircraft or systems)	5

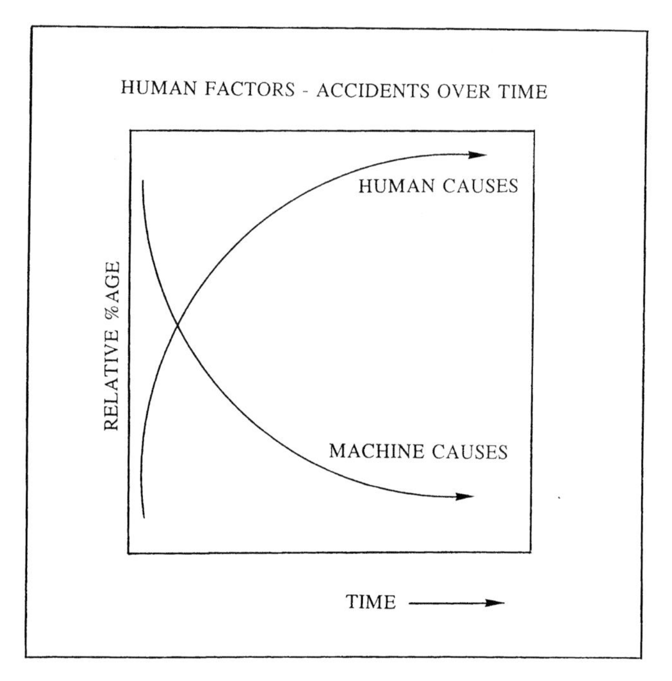

Figure 6

It is estimated that there is one catastrophe per million take-offs. Can we say that this is a problem? If the answer is no, then there is no doubt that the industry still has a responsibility continually to improve safety.

No one can put a monetary value on human life, although the courts try to when apportioning blame relating to disasters where there is loss of life. Staff morale must be upheld with as much effort as goes into the preservation of the travelling public's confidence.

Significant crew cause factors and percentage of presence in 93 major accidents 1977–1984*

Percentage
33% Pilot deviated from basic operational procedures
26% Inadequate cross-check by second crew member
9% Crews not conditioned for proper response in abnormal conditions
6% Pilot did not recognise the need for go-around
4% Pilot incapacitation

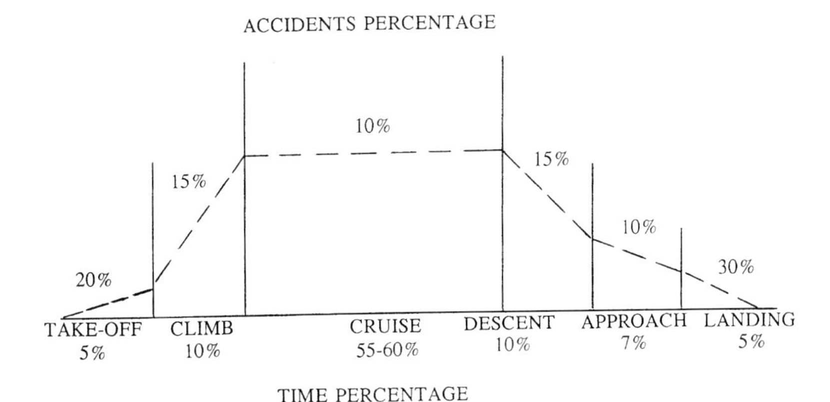

Figure 7 Human factors – accidents over time
(Statistical data mid-1980s, average figures)

4% Inadequate piloting skills
3% Pilot used improper procedure during go-around
3% Crew errors during training flight
3% Pilot not trained to respond promptly to ground proximity
3% Procedures did not require use of available approach aids
3% Captain inexperienced in aircraft type
*HULL LOSS AND FATAL ACCIDENTS

The United States National Transport Safety Board (NTSB) figures put human factors at the top of the list in relation to accident statistics:

HUMAN FACTORS	73%
WEATHER	11%
AIRCRAFT	11%
OTHERS	11%
MINOR TECHNICAL	43%
CLEAR TECH LOG	57%

Some significant human factor categories

It should be understood that the cause of accidents cannot be directly related to any single specific human factor. This is simply because HF accidents are typically multi-cause. However, the following list gives a good cross-section of some primary causes worth studying (there are of course many more):

- cockpit distractions
- attention slips
- degraded situational awareness
- fatigue (resulting in under-performance)
- automation
- understanding
- mistaken intentions/misunderstanding
- false hypothesis
- indecisiveness
- co-ordination and communication problems
- lack of crew co-ordination and team skills
- conflict resolution
- a variety of stressors

To give us a perspective of accidents in percentage terms:

Accident causes in 119 fatal accidents 1977–1988

41% Inadequate communication
37% Crew deviated from standard operating procedures (SOP)
15% Maintenance deficiency
12% No ground proximity warning system (GPWS) or inadequate crew response
11% Design deficiencies
11% Inadequate training
9% Inadequate approach aids
9% Runway hazards
9% Weather information
6% Flight operations procedures inadequate

Summary

An overview of the total package

Hardware Aircraft type, instrumentation, warning systems, controls, auto-pilot, auto-throttle, advanced avionics and supporting computers.

Software Aircraft operations manuals (SOP), checklists, maps and charts with appropriate technical information.

Liveware The human component of this computer system, together with other inter-related and accessible people in the system.

Environment Involves the social crew discipline and crew discord, plus the physical aspects, noise, variations in temperature, turbulence and the interaction with air traffic control.

We must keep in the forefront of our minds that Human Factors (HF) and Crew Resource Management (CRM) are first and foremost when it comes to preventing aircraft accidents.

Chapter 9
Safety Saves Money

Adherence to laid down procedures is the greatest single accident prevention strategy identified in a study of accidents. Companies which actively promote good safety within their organisations not only save lives, but in the longer term save money, which ultimately helps the balance sheet.

We hear a great deal about safety in the aviation industry generally, let alone the promotion of CRM involving cockpit safety management specifically, which is what this book is all about. But we have to ask ourselves, what does safety *really* mean? We are constantly urged by the regulators and the public to ensure we have the safest operations we can. This is all very well, but *how* do we get there?

Let's probe this a little further. Question number one: Is your company profitable? If the answer is yes, how do you know? Probably because the official balance sheet shows there is more money coming in than going out. The balance sheet may even show a tidy profit – in aviation terms, that is. Now the second question: Is the operation I am flying for really safe? If the answer is yes, how do you know? Is it simply the fact you haven't had any accidents? The 'zero accident' statistic taken in isolation is not a conclusive indication of a safe operation.

Unsafe practices are potential accidents

I have seen pilots get away with some incredibly unsafe practices, for example cutting down fuel reserves to unacceptable levels, which in effect means no contingency planning: 'playing it by ear' in flight planning; in other words, not taking into account the full implications of adverse weather, availability of navigation and instrument let-down aids, as well as suitability of alternative airfields.

The fact that the operation has never had an accident doesn't mean it is safe – it means it's been lucky. What we really need to examine are the actions, not the outcomes, to determine if it is safe or not. We have to examine all our actions and decisions, in and out of the cockpit. That is how we can tell if we have a safe operation or not. This is all part of the safety evaluation process. You might wonder why I'm bothering to go into this subject in such detail.

Well the answer to this is fairly simple and straightforward: I've almost killed myself on several occasions (in my early flying days) due to the influence of such pilots, at that time senior to me. Many of them are now dead.

Aircraft operators, whether regular airline or just a small charter company, have a moral obligation to make safety their number one priority. In general terms, relatively few people are killed in aviation accidents, compared to fatalities on the road. Nevertheless, one fatality in aviation is one too many. A well-thought-out company safety performance will minimise the possibility that you will have an accident.

The drastic effects of accidents

Another compelling reason for minimising accident and incident potential is financial. The direct costs of an accident, or even a simple incident, can be ruinous. Firstly there is the cost of injuries, damage to hardware and property. The other major item is insurance. It is certainly a myth that the insurance company will pay for everything. There is always a deductible which will vary with the size of the aircraft.

The costs mentioned here are obviously easy to identify. It is the indirect costs that are much harder to quantify, but they are staggering when added up. Indirect costs include things such as reduced operating capability, lost revenues, schedule changes, overtime and lost work time. Then if you think about it, what does everybody do when there is an accident? Answer: they stand around and look at it! You could call it 'accident malaise' (a type of mental apathy), which is quite a common occurrence in such circumstances. The direct costs of an accident or incident mount up, and can easily exceed a staggering four times the direct costs.

Negative customer reaction

Another major indirect cost is termed 'negative customer reaction'; if people (the public) think your airline is unsafe they will travel on another carrier. Believe me, this is a real world phenomenon, and it can have far-reaching commercial effects on an operating company. It was reported in the London *Financial Times* and the European *Wall Street Journal* on 25 October 1994 that the American airline USAir attributed $US 40 million of the $US 180 million they lost in the third quarter of 1994 to negative customer reaction. This was the direct association with the two fatal crashes that occurred two months apart in the same year. Public reaction was therefore rapid and financially damaging.

The safety programme highlights procedural errors

Safety can be defined as freedom from risk or danger. The main problem is that the whole world is full of hazards, including aviation. Due to this fact, we have developed a set of rules, policies, procedures and practices that manage those risks and help assure that the aviation system is relatively free of danger.

The philosophy of safety has thoroughly ingrained itself at the airline level:

- flight operations departments produce operations manuals for aircrew that set out (safe) procedures
- maintenance departments use maintenance manuals and task cards to maintain and repair aircraft in accordance with regulations and the manufacturer's recommendations
- the training department makes sure all staff (aircrew and ground) adheres to the rules and safe procedures

Each company safety programme has a unique function. It establishes processes for highlighting deviations from procedures, or indeed where there is no procedure at all. Understanding these deviations is important. Often the only factor separating a near miss, a deviation and an accident is an alert crew. The near miss tells the company that something is not quite right in a number of areas. The time to tackle the problems is in the early (minor) stages, not after a major accident.

The traditional elements of safety

A quick look at the elements of safety will show us the process of finding out about deviations:

- mandatory reporting
- inspections
- audits
- investigations

Of course, there are others. But all of these processes are intended to alert the management that some condition or action is not meeting the prescribed standard. So now let's get back to the original question. How do we know if we are safe? It isn't something we can positively quantify. The answer surely lies with processes, meaning the company with the ability to establish and follow standards will go a long way towards being safe.

Establish standards everyone can follow

Having made sure you have set standards that everyone can follow, *train* everyone to follow them. Although rules and procedures are not always perfect, they do help establish an acceptable level of safety. Frequently we look at rules, regulations and procedures as something of a nuisance, whose sole objective is to limit our ability to make money. In a Boeing Aircraft Company study of one hundred and twenty aircraft accidents, they found adherence to procedures as the single greatest accident prevention strategy. There are many reasons given for not following procedures:

- they never knew them
- forgot them
- used the wrong one
- chose the right one and did it wrongly
- purposely did not follow it

The Russians have twice identified intentional rule violations as the leading cause of accidents in Russia and the Commonwealth of Independent States (1992 and 1995). If it comes down to economics or safety that is a management decision, and the stated policy must be safety first with economics second.

Management involvement

The supervision of any company safety programme is the most important part. If there is no management support the programme will certainly fail. Management support has two basic elements: structural and personal.

Strive to be cost-effective

Like any problem, you cannot simply throw money at it and hope that will solve it, because in most cases it doesn't. One of the best ways of management dealing with safety and safety issues, I found, was SBWA, which translates to Safety By Wandering Around. The recommendation is that the manager walks around and talks to people about safety. Do they have any particular problems? Is everything going all right? This approach is very effective, because the working level employees *see* that the boss is as interested in safety as in the company purely making a profit without regard to other issues.

The manager should review all incident and accident data for his company. He must know and keep up to date with what is going on. If the manager doesn't get involved, or worse still doesn't care about safety, the rest of the employees will soon find out and very quickly act accordingly. Should this happen then that manager could be faced with some real problems.

You might think that at first glance a safety programme could end up costing your company some serious money. The answer to that is both yes and no: yes, because it does take time and significant effort; and no, because with a little thought and organisation (being careful about wastage) safety programmes can be very cost-effective. One very senior insurance executive once said to me, 'If you think promoting and administering safety is expensive, try paying for an accident!'

CHAPTER 10

LEARNING SAFETY LESSONS

Safety in the cockpit is one of the most essential ingredients to a safe flight. Crew teamwork and good resource management need constant work and attention.

Coping with automation

Automated systems are becoming so computer-orientated that it needs real concentration to understand what is really going on. Between INS, EFIS, autopilots, digital engine computers, digital FMS and all the rest of the paraphernalia, any flightcrew certainly has its hands full of 'technology'. This has to be properly managed in order to ensure an effective and safe flight.

Many pilots have had to learn safety lessons as they went along with their everyday flight duties. Unfortunately there have been some catastrophic mistakes made while trying to do this. Without the proper knowledge and correct programming of some of these systems, tragedy is often not far away; consider the JAL 747 that was shot down after it strayed off course, or the chartered DC-10 on a sightseeing flight to the Antarctic that crashed through automated navigation error. In 1981, an Air New Zealand DC-10 crashed into Mt Erebus after incorrect navigation data had been entered into the computer by (would you believe) ground personnel.

Another tragedy happened to a China Airlines Boeing 747 in 1985, over the Pacific Ocean. There was a slow loss of power in the number four engine. The autopilot tried to hold heading and altitude, but eventually caused a stall followed by a spin. Another one involved a United Airlines DC-8 at Portland in 1978. In this case the aircraft actually ran out of fuel and crashed short of the runway. Cause: cockpit distractions leading to a breakdown in cockpit communications about the fuel state. In other words, the captain failed to make timely and effective decisions. This is because he, or his crew, did not use established CRM practices.

The most probable cause of the first three accidents was blamed on human error in loading (programming) the navigation computers. In the case of China Airlines, the automated systems were apparently allowed to overcome good crew cockpit management procedures at the expense of safety. Such

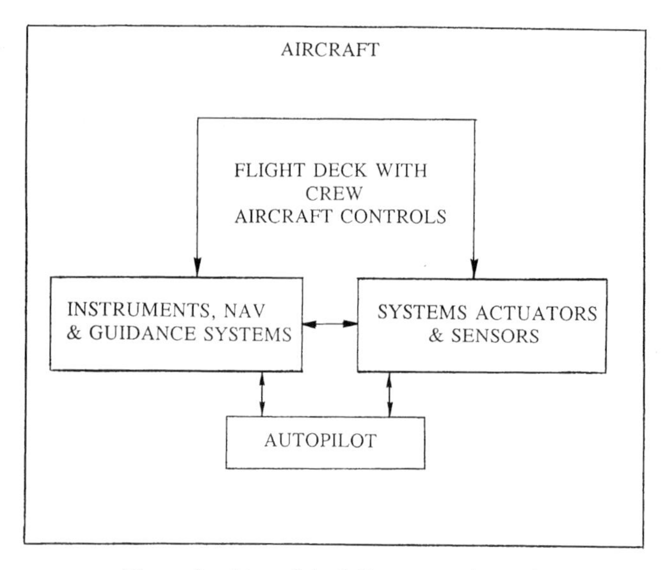

Figure 8 Aircraft in fully automatic mode

apparently simple mistakes needlessly cost the lives of hundreds of people. It can of course prove a tiresome business, loading a large number of waypoints into a single, dual or triplex navigation computer system. One slip of the finger can result in the aircraft (and several hundred unsuspecting passengers) heading off into the wild blue yonder, in entirely the wrong direction.

Defining automation

This is not quite as straightforward as you might think, simply because there are various definitions of automation, and different levels.

We can say the first one is 'the replacement of manual tasks by machines of one sort or another'. This varies from a simple two-axis autopilot (as fitted to many light aircraft) right through to the three-axis modern autopilot system that has the capability of flying the aircraft from take-off to landing, with no help from the pilot. A second definition refers to cockpit data presented on cathode ray tubes (EFIS), replacing mechanical or electromechanical instruments. This is the glass cockpit now being installed in almost all modern airliners. Flight information, navigation and other systems are presented on computer screens.

A third area of automation is offered by on-board computers, INS, Area Navigation, Loran C and such. These have been designed to relieve pilots of navigation uncertainty and stress in unfamiliar or remote areas. A fourth level of automation concerns the important area of cockpit monitoring and alerting systems. Some of these are aural (bells, buzzers), others visual (lights, either steady or flashing). They alert the pilot to positions, altitudes or cautionary and emergency (systems) situations. One very good warning system is GPWS, Ground Proximity Warning System, not now confined to large passenger aircraft.

In the Fully Automatic Mode aircraft, the workload is low and the crew is mostly out of the control system. Many experienced pilots complain that automation reduces them to 'administrative flight managers', thus taking away many of their basic traditional professional pilot functions, which leaves them with poor job satisfaction. Deep down, mentally, they regard what is really 'computer control' as not being as safe as a flight when the human pilot has full control. Therefore opinion seems to indicate that poor satisfaction can only lead to poor pilot performance.

Automation has many advantages

Having looked at the downside, automation does have a variety of advantages in the cockpit:

- it can take over many continuous control tasks
- the pilot has more freedom for important functions such as decision-making
- helps safety by removing the human error link within the cockpit environment, and replacing it with more reliable machines (This argument carries some weight among aviation safety experts, since pilot error accounts for such a considerably high number of the total accidents.)

There are other advantages to automation, one of which is the reduction in the crew size (although many aviation training experts have argued against this for safety reasons). It also results in smoother control of the aircraft, and takes better care of fuel management, thereby helping to reduce operating costs. Computer-controlled displays give more options for presenting information, which can be quickly and easily accessed by the crew. In the semi-automatic mode there are some real advantages if we consider human factors. The aircrew stay in the control system via the autopilot, which either of two pilots can use to initiate such additional manoeuvres as increasing or decreasing rates of turn, plus climbs and descents.

Increase in human factor errors

During the course of this current decade, safety investigators have come up with some alarming results concerning crew error. They discovered that during critical situations and in-flight emergencies, at least one crew member had vital information which could have solved the problem.

Any accident is a tragic event, but if the information resources are available to prevent catastrophe – whether this be unrecognised, misunderstood, ignored or not presented by a crew member for whatever reason – then some serious remedial action has to be taken.

Another accident highlights this perfectly. An Eastern Airlines L-1011, location Miami, 1972. The aircraft descended straight into the Everglades while the crew was distracted, in this case to a very high degree, trying to sort out a landing gear problem that turned out to be a blown electric bulb.

Practise safety management

This is where safety management and crew resource management are extremely important for the best interests of everyone. So what are the safety lessons we must learn? Obviously we must confirm the integrity of the information put into the computers by double-checking everything. We can do this by comparing one computer's waypoints against those of the other, if you have a double or triple system. The co-pilot is the best person to do this if you programmed the system yourself, otherwise vice versa. Naturally this must be done using an official waypoint chart, Jeppesen, Aerad or similar.

Safety is also having both crew members knowing the aircraft's exact position *at all times*. Every pilot has a tendency to flick a switch, or turn a knob without mentioning it to the other pilot or crew member. Flying is not supposed to be a guessing game for the pilot in the other seat; let the other crew member know what you are doing *when you do it*. Good inter-crew communication (and communication generally) plays such an important role in flight safety, that ignoring it can lead to multiple problems. How many times have we read in accident reports that the determining cause was 'the failure of crew communication and co-ordination'. It doesn't cost you anything to communicate.

Setting and maintaining safe standards

Setting achievable standards and conforming to safe policies is one way of learning safety lessons. Adhering to the principles of Crew Resource

Management in conjunction with Line Orientated Flight Training (LOFT) helps improve proficiency and develop safer operating procedures.

Reviewing a crew's performance on video tape after simulator training helps reach better standard operating procedures, crew co-ordination and communication. This is particularly important in dealing with emergency situations.

Standardisation is the lynch-pin to learning safety lessons. Policy, practice and procedure is what all of us should continue to strive for each time we go to fly. There is nothing worse than watching two pilots in a simulated emergency situation on the flight deck, with all four hands flashing about pushing buttons and moving switches *before* the emergency checklist is reviewed! This is entirely the wrong way of promoting safety in the cockpit. We *must* learn the safety lessons.

Striving for improved performance

The US National Transportation and Safety Board (NTSB) has studied advancing cockpit automation for some time. Safety experts believe that this technology does, and will continue to, save time and reduce pilot workload, but only if we (the aircrew) fully understand the new systems. The NTSB summarised its findings by saying that 'it believed the history of accidents and incidents involving automation versus safety dictates the need for some remedial action'. It added that 'extensive research findings regarding the overall effects of automation on flight crew proficiency and performance reinforce the need for improved pilot procedures and pilot training programmes'. Which means improving safety by learning safety lessons.

Human performance factors

Statistics show that the human element in the cockpit, if not the weak link in the system, is certainly the most unpredictable and prone to making errors. The types of errors are familiar to us all:

- failure to monitor altitude
- violation of Decision Height (DH)
- inadequate supervision of laid down flight procedures
- failure to exercise positive flight management

Having said all this, what we need to tackle is the question of why the human failure occurred in the first place. In other words, how it was *allowed* to happen. Even from these few examples (and there are unfortunately many more), we can see there is a continual need to improve procedures, pilot training and standardisation, and to learn the safety lessons.

Multi-crew co-ordination in LOFT procedures

Practical training requirements have been established by ECAC, the European Civil Aviation Conference, in the planned development towards harmonisation of pilot licensing within Europe. The following extract is an *interpreted* guide to the instruction syllabus that should be followed.

1. Crew co-ordination concept, objectives, allocation of tasks between the Flying Pilot (FP) and Non-Flying Pilot (NFP).
2. The use of checklists under normal, abnormal and emergency conditions. Mutual supervision, information and general support. Inter-crew 'call-out' procedures.
3. Pre-flight preparation, flight planning, aircraft documentation including weight and balance (loading) and computation of take-off performance data.
4. All normal pre-flight checks for the aircraft type, radio and navigation equipment, ensuring correct settings.
5. Taxi, and power plant checks, pre-take-off checks. Crew take-off briefing by FP.
6. Normal take-offs with various flap settings, tasks and call-outs, FP and NFP.
7. Rejected (aborted take-offs prior to V1). Crosswind take-offs at maximum all-up weight (MAUW) for the conditions. Engine failure after V1.
8. Use of checklists. Normal and abnormal operation of aircraft systems commensurate with safety.
9. Emergency procedures, including simulated engine failure, fire, smoke control and removal. Action to tackle windshear during take-off and landing.
10. Incapacitation of a flight crew member and emergency descent procedures.
11. Early recognition of and positive reaction to an impending stall with different aircraft configurations. (Strict adherence to type procedures is essential.)
12. Instrument flight procedures including holding, ILS using raw navigational data, plus full flight director and automatic pilot (as appropriate during the training procedure). Simulated engine-out approaches, VOR,

NDB, DME or a combination as required. Circle to land approaches. Approach briefing by FP, setting up of nav/approach aids by NFP. Review of call-out procedures during the various approaches. Checklists.

13. Go-arounds (missed approach procedures), normal and engine-out. Also rejected landing from predetermined decision height (DH), normal or asymmetric.
14. Normal and crosswind landings, and with simulated engine-out (asymmetric). Crew co-operation during transition from instrument to visual flight, and/or after reaching DH or MDA. Support by NFP.
15. Skill test with emphasis on the application of the crew co-ordination concept.

This is the current thinking in broad terms. But all training organisations and particularly Training Captains and instructors will understand there are no simple answers to crew co-ordination problems, merely tried and tested procedures through a professional approach to the whole subject:

- whether single- or multi-crew, it is essential that cockpit tasks are considered in relation to time
- pilots have become distracted and confused at critical moments because of a sudden and mainly self-imposed task loading
- the primary task has to be concentrated on *controlling* and *flying* the aircraft (this is a dangerous time because additional, but essential cockpit tasks may be tackled in the wrong order or, worse still, missed completely; there is also the strong possibility of mis-selection of various system controls)
- abnormal and emergency checklists must be used at any time during a simulated or real emergency situation
- the crew (particularly the pilot in command) must be ahead of the aircraft to stay in control of the situation; anything less will create the opportunity for making mistakes
- plan ahead and complete the required tasks at the right time; the possibility of making mistakes will be reduced and good situational awareness will be maintained

Motivation, dedication, concentration, communication, the correct use of checklists, and a genuine desire to improve proficiency: this is what is required. Every pilot, whatever the status (rank) differentials, must put aside pre-judgement of others. When, or if, doubts exist in whatever context within the training syllabus, then communication and satisfactory resolution must follow.

In general terms, both management and line pilots have welcomed the new subjects included in CRM training such as skills, stress, standard operating procedures (SOPs) and character, as well as the study of personality and attitudes. These are felt to bring a meaningful new source of useful information to the wider aspects of the whole subject.

Overcoming problem cockpits

Completing all the required tasks in a less than 'user friendly' cockpit has been a problem for decades. Unfortunately it is difficult for designers to come up with something that will satisfactorily accommodate the varying sizes of pilots. The main stumbling block has been financial constraints. Many of the 'built-in' pitfalls of badly placed switches and system controls have been rearranged for reasons of safety, but overall, commercial expediency has taken precedence over human factors. However, pilots are reasonably adaptable and able to live with design inadequacies. In the future, though, the closer the cockpit fits man's needs, the more the possibility of pilots making mistakes diminishes.

Ten flight safety commandments

- Always ensure someone is flying the aircraft.
- If in doubt about anything, assume the worst and check again.
- Make sure the entire crew is on the same mental wavelength.
- Never move a lever or switch unless you inform another crew member you have done it.
- Never use a non-standard procedure because it leads to confusion; follow the official checklists.
- If you make an error, admit it – trying to cover it up can be worse.
- Never fly with out-of-date maps and charts, something critical is bound to have changed.
- Concentrate on maintaining good personal situational awareness at all times.
- Always follow the clearance you are given.
- Double-check minimum safety altitudes, minimum descent altitudes and review all instrument approach procedures in plenty of time.

Finally, let us not forget the 11th Commandment: aviate, navigate, communicate, checklist.

Chapter 11
Feedback from the Flight Crews (CHIRP)

Confidential Human Incident Reporting

In the United Kingdom the Confidential Human Incident Reporting Programme, run by the Institute of Aviation Medicine, Farnborough, provides a valuable method of gaining more knowledge on human factor errors. A clear line has to be drawn between the human errors resulting from incompetence, a lack of ability, inadequate training and the limitations of human performance. We all know that there is a limit to what humans can do, and everyone suffers from illusions of three-dimensional perception. Just because an airline captain has been flying for thirty years and has 20,000 flying hours, brings no immunity from these human limitations. Particular series of circumstances result in pushing an individual towards psychological limits which are common to all human beings.

Awareness versus human error

Human error has one big problem: the individual fails to recognise the error when it is happening, otherwise it is a logical assumption the person committing the error would take action to overcome it. Therefore it follows that awareness of problems goes a long way to the avoidance of errors, but not entirely. It is also true to say that one person can often identify faults that can lead to errors being made by another person. But that person is unaware of any fault in himself.

In flying, as in other professions, errors are taking place every day while carrying out a whole series of different tasks. However, the individuals do not notice it – they are unaware. The worst part is that when the error is plain for all to see, the person who has committed the error is not aware of the reality of what has happened, only what will result or is resulting.

Perceiving problem areas

Perception of a problem is the key area of human factors. Everyone sees a particular situation differently from another person, this is basic human make-up. Even technical facts may be perceived and evaluated differently by different sets of pilots. What the management sees as one small problem in the wider concept of company operations is viewed entirely differently by a captain facing the same technical unserviceability which had grounded the aircraft for which he is responsible.

Levels of training, intellectual knowledge and expertise vary considerably in the strata of pilots from GA up to large commercial airlines. This has to be perceived as having some significance when considering human limitations. It shows there is an obvious variation between both individual pilots and groups of pilots, and other variations within the groups. There will be a whole range of different behaviours in individual cockpits for different environments. All this has to be taken into consideration and examined.

Problem-solving solutions

Sticking to standard operating procedures (SOP), using checklists and concentrating on good inter-personal crew relationships and situational awareness, plus good communication on the flight deck, will help solve problems. Not only that, it might well prevent many happening in the first place.

In today's modern cockpit there are unfortunately much greater time constraints. The result of this means that each pilot is required to complete the different tasks in that available time. This of course causes monitoring levels to suffer. The following four reports form interesting and informative case studies that can be analysed in conjunction with other CRM work.

Report 1: Error on ATC clearance
AIRCRAFT HOLDING AT FL80.
Clearance to leave the hold given by ATC. Roughly – 'Return to Fix and leave heading 270 degrees speed 210 kts.'

I read this back. R/T very busy at this time. Capt said we had also been cleared to FL70. I did not hear this. So I read back 'and FL70'. I may have omitted to use our call-sign – also there is a strong possibility that on transmission I crossed with another a/c. I should have made another transmission

to check and I should have used proper R/T phraseology. I should have been more prepared to question a clearance I did not hear myself.
ACTION: On reaching FL70 ATC instructed to climb to FL80. Discussed with ATC who confirmed no risk of conflict. I am still not sure if mistake was ATC's or mine.

Report 2. Chronic fatigue
At outstation on turn-round, pax boarding delayed due inefficient handling agent, F/O and I sitting on flight deck waiting. I realise F/O is unusually quiet and when I look at him he's almost fallen asleep!!
Discussions with another captain reveal he's had similar situation (with different F/O) while airborne!

Why should our F/Os be so tired? – because our salary scales mean that many of them find it necessary to take second jobs (e.g. driving or painting and decorating) in order for them to pay their mortgages and repay the loans they have taken out to finance their flying licences.

While I accept the laws of economics and supply and demand give no incentive for our employer to raise the salary, and indeed a big rise would threaten the company's profitability, etc., I think we are taken too much for granted and not rewarded for the professional licences we have trained for and financed ourselves.

P.S. I very nearly didn't write this report as I think there is too much whingeing and whining in many companies and I am actually grateful to hold the position I do, but safety must surely be compromised here.

Report 3. Cumulative fatigue
I had had two early mornings (getting up before 0600 local) on the 3rd and 4th May to do two European flights and I was rostered for a 1900L–0500L standby the following day. On the 5th May I got up at 0830L and did not sleep again that day. At 1900L crewing phoned to call me in for a UK–EUROPE–UK on which the rostered crew were already into discretion.

Due to complication with dual rating the plan was to stand the original F/O down and I should fly to EUROPE with Capt A (rostered) operating and another captain (called from standby) on the jumpseat. On turn-round Capt. A went on to the jumpseat. Capt. B from another base was operating captain, I was F/O (PNF), and the captain we brought down returned to that other UK base in a different aircraft.

All went according to plan and I still felt fine as we set off from EUROPE for the UK (0300L). As always with three pilots on the flight deck there was more stimulation and conversation than usual and I didn't start to feel jaded until the last ninety minutes of the flight. With one hour to go I really started to feel tired but thought I should be able to last the flight without falling asleep. At the top of descent my eyes closed for the first time and I was in somewhat of a dozy state during the descent. I still felt, however, that I could make a big final effort during the last ten minutes of the flight when there was more activity. Going downwind for landing, the approach checks, RT calls and then flap setting did increase the activity but I simply felt worse than ever. Commands/actions were followed immediately by falling asleep again. On final approach I found myself being woken up as the captain was asking for gear down, flaps, etc. When we finally landed I felt dreadful and possibly the worst in six years of IT flying.

There are obvious safety implications from this incident, not the least of which was my driving home (0830L) afterwards. The irony of the situation was that the two pilots in discretion had been accommodated by crewing and felt fine whereas I was still within my allowed FDP and felt like death. I think that standby duties during late evening/early morning are almost impossible to rest and prepare for properly but can be acceptable with good rostering. I swear I will never accept an early morning duty followed by late evening standby on the roster again.

Report 4: Circadian disrhythmia

CAPTAIN'S COMMENT: This was a return flight from West Coast, USA with a night departure. My P2 was handling the return sector from the West Coast USA to the UK.

In good weather (visibility 5 km with a layer of Strato-Cu 2,000 ft to 5,000 ft) briefed for ILS approach to R/W 12L. Approaching the hold, approach turned us on to southerly heading earlier than expected, which placed us slightly high but with use of speedbrake and careful monitoring of vertical profile should be OK. ATC then advised us that our runway would be 12R and continued to vector for ILS. I became preoccupied with the VERTICAL profile and asked the captain to set up 12R in the FMS, but due to preoccupation with vertical profile I forgot to select correct frequency for ILS 12R. Established on ILS localiser and glideslope simultaneously at 2,500 ft when ATC queried if we were on localiser for 12R and reminded us of the correct frequency. We realised our mistake and fortunately at that moment broke cloud and were able to visually manoeuvre for 12R.

We often get a late change of runway so why did we get it wrong this time?

1. The route off the hold placed us high and fast so we became preoccupied with getting on to the vertical profile.

2. Preoccupation with that FMS instead of basic ILS tuning.
3. Maybe ATC could have reminded us of the correct ILS frequency when first giving the runway change.

Thank you to an alert radar controller who saved three very red faces from a serious incident.

CHAPTER 12

SAFETY VERSUS THE 'RAMBO' COMPLEX

The consequence of irresponsible actions

We live in today's modern, technologically advancing world, where the importance of all human roles and ambitious goals are being constantly reappraised. We have to live with the knowledge that any of our individual actions do not take place in isolation. In reality, every action to a greater or lesser extent affects the lives and well-being of others. Just one moment of irresponsible action can lead to the death of another person, perhaps even destroy many thousands of people, or alter the balance of nature and leave a legacy of disaster for generations to come.

What exists now is a sensitively balanced state of technological and social interdependence. Even the actions of an individual can result in repercussions and changes in society and nature that cannot be predicted or controlled. No one has told us what *really* happened at Chernobyl. All we can say is the disaster was certainly caused by a variety of human factors, a 'chain of mistakes' and the inability to make the right decisions for a whole variety of reasons; ultimately, man's inability to control his own technology. For instance, World War II resulted in profound and far-reaching changes that still affect all of us, even today. The Vietnam conflict changed the thinking of an entire nation. One man with a distorted ambition for power was responsible for the Gulf War, and all the drama that it created. The fall-out is still with us. Many leaders and academics believe that the break-up of the former Soviet Union has left a more dangerous potential threat of nuclear disaster than ever before. Churchill once said, 'beware the sleeping giant', meaning China. We have yet to see what happens with that vast, densely populated country in the twenty-first century.

So what can we conclude from all this? One thing we can deduce is that in spite of all man's technological advances, he knows little more about himself than he did two hundred years ago. This lack of knowledge has produced some dangerous traits. One of these has been generally accepted without question by the majority.

The machismo complex

Leaving aside aviation for the moment, let's look at a scenario that easily explains what I mean. At a well known skiing area in the French Alps, a mixed nationality group of teenagers, aged sixteen to nineteen years, decide to race down a long mountain slope. All the youths are competent skiers. The race starts, and after the first few hundred metres the eldest (who is unofficially regarded as the leader) starts to drop behind. This encourages him to take a shorter route that has been designated a danger area. It has hidden rocks and is hazardously steep. At this point he has only one thought in his mind – to get ahead of the others and win the race. The fact that he is placing himself in an extremely dangerous situation does not seem to have been considered. For a short time it appears as if he will get away with it as he jumps, twists and turns with supreme confidence. Then disaster strikes. He misjudges the jump over a large boulder and hits the top at 50 mph. The impact kills him instantly.

Now let's consider an aviation situation. The 'enemy' in this case is the weather, or is it? The location is a regional airport beside a coastal town which is a popular summer tourist resort. Consequently, there are busy early morning and late evening commuter flight schedules. Two early morning F27 flights from rival airlines are due to arrive within fifteen minutes of each other, but the airport is fogbound. The weather is below the minima of both companies and that of the airport.

In spite of this, the first F27 decides to make the VOR/DME approach but fails to get in. During the missed approach procedure ATC informs the captain there is a slight improvement in the visibility, although it is still below the company minima. The aircraft manages to land at the second attempt. A few minutes later the second F27 arrives overhead and the controller passes the latest weather actual, informing the captain that the first aircraft has already landed. By now the visibility has dropped again, and if anything, is worse than before. In spite of the situation, the captain decides to make an approach to 'have a look' and doesn't start the missed approach procedure until he is almost 100 feet below the 320 feet MDA. He makes a second attempt and the controller catches a fleeting glimpse of the aircraft halfway down the runway. It is 200 feet below the MDA. At the third attempt to land only the sound of the turbo-prop engines are heard, then there is a sudden explosion and a brief orange-yellow glow is seen through the fog.

The F27 was so low it had crashed into the main building of a hotel close to the beach. The structure was only fifty feet high and to one side of the extended runway centreline on the approach. Thirty-four people in the hotel were killed and twenty injured. A tourist bus loading passengers in the adjacent car park miraculously escaped the disaster. The F27 crew died, as did all twenty-seven passengers and two female flight attendants.

Now let's analyse these two cases. In the skiing scenario the nineteen-year-old had to win at all costs to prove himself the best. He ignored the fact he was taking a dangerous chance. This is the machismo complex at work; subconsciously his manhood was at stake. When we consider the actions of the two F27 captains, we have to review a variety of different factors that led up to the final disaster. Both pilots were under commercial pressure to land in spite of the weather, whatever the official regulations stated. The first captain took a chance and managed to get in because he was lucky, and was able to take advantage of a short temporary increase in visibility. The second F27 captain had both increased commercial pressure and additional stress thrust upon him by the successful actions of the first captain. The fact that on the third and final (disastrous) approach he was significantly to one side of the centreline showed how the increased (cockpit) stress had affected his professional flying skills. This complete disregard for safety was therefore brought about by the desire not to show a loss of manhood, and commercial pressures intensified by rivalry and self-imposed (cockpit) stress. We also have to take into account the fact that neither co-pilot did anything to prevent what happened. It seems that they could not express the fear they felt to each captain as they went below the MDA; any action they took would have been going against the grain of their manhood.

So what *is* this problem of safety versus manhood? There is no doubt it can occur at any age in many different jobs and activities. What we do know is that it peaks in teenagers and young adults. However, there have been isolated flashes of it returning in the mid to late fifties. (The reasons for this, though, are slightly more complex.) Proving manhood to the detriment of safety is one of the main reasons why young adults have so many accidents. In fact it is one of the major single causes of accidents in this age group. This now applies equally to young women due to their increasingly assertive role in society.

We see this manhood-machismo syndrome come to the forefront in war. Soldiers, sailors and airmen who are suddenly caught up in the heat of battle perform heroic deeds without any thought for their personal safety, and it wasn't until a year after the First World War had started that the steel helmet (or 'tin hat' as it was known) was developed. It was certainly not popular at first. One British General was so incensed by what he thought of as the 'suspect moral fibre of the troops that wore them', he issued a general order which read: 'Any soldier in my command wearing a tin hat will be court-martialled for cowardice in the face of the enemy.' The General got away with it, but by the end of the war steel helmets were in wide use – at least for front-line troops.

Having said all this, what about the airlines? If we consider it no one wants to think about accidents, least of all the airlines by publicising the subject in any way. Can you imagine the advertising slogan, 'Fly on our airline, we are the least liable to have an accident.' If that happened, not only would it scare potential passengers (many of the public are nervous of flying as it is), the public might think the *airline* was scared. It perhaps sounds a little far-fetched, but there's more than a few grains of truth in the points raised here.

Safety planning and safety precautions are always treated in a very subdued, low-key fashion. This is borne out when we consider the safety information card that's tucked away in a seat pocket – single sheet, narrow, monotonously routine, you could say. Perhaps it should be larger and dramatised with eye-catching 'day-glo' lettering:

- READ THIS CARD *NOW* IN CASE WE CRASH!
- LEARN WHERE THE SAFETY EXITS ARE, IT COULD SAVE YOUR LIFE
- OBEY THE CABIN ATTENDANT'S INSTRUCTIONS, IT WILL GREATLY IMPROVE YOUR CHANCES OF SURVIVAL
- MENTALLY PREPARE YOURSELF FOR AN EMERGENCY BY REVIEWING THE OTHER INFORMATION ON THIS CARD REGULARLY THROUGHOUT THE FLIGHT

– and so on. Over the top? Maybe. Truthful, certainly. But no one really wants to hear the truth in such stark terms.

Then comes the pre-flight safety briefing from the flight attendants, backed up by a pre-recorded commentary. Even this is being widely superseded by the safety briefing taking the form of a short film shown on the in-flight video system. The sanitised commentary is generally given by a smiling, good-looking (usually female) flight attendant in calm, evenly paced, well-modulated tones. This is preceded by the commentator saying, 'Government regulations require that all passengers . . .' as if they are attempting to apologise for disturbing us with such distasteful information. In fact it wasn't until the end of the first decade of the twentieth century that any real safety legislation came into force. And only this was passed after several high-profile accidents with heavy (and avoidable) loss of life. The public *demanded* such protection.

Now we are getting to the heart of the problem. If we are somehow able to accept that it is macho genuinely to take notice of our own safety, not pay lip service to it, we have made a considerable leap forward. If we protect ourselves we are also protecting others. This is no more apparent than in flying. Manhood should only be demonstrated by taking wise operational decisions, not following the F27 scenario described earlier in this chapter.

Regulatory authority, workload and safety

There is a general acceptance that it is necessary to have a large degree of 'regulatory pressure' exerted on aviation operations, mostly to ensure that safe operating practices are being observed. Safety also demands strict observance of regulations and procedures, including all pre-flight technical inspections of the aircraft, and the evaluation of the pilot's ability to conduct the flight in the particular conditions.

Regulatory authorities should always consider the overall impact of new regulations and procedures relating to safety. These can have a profound and far-reaching effect on the workloads on pilots, engineers, operations staff, air traffic controllers, and many others. New regulations written in offices mostly by administrative, policy and legal staff may not be compatible with the real world of aviation 'operations'.

Safety is the usual reason for creating new rules. Is it not a fact, though, that many are made to utilise airspace in a better, more efficient way for commercial as well as safety considerations? The object after all is to minimise the human error factor, which is a more difficult objective to achieve with the increasing complexity of airspace divisions. Because of this all personnel involved in aircraft operations have had increased work and psychological demands placed upon them year by year. With the annual increase in air traffic worldwide, we have to raise our awareness of the failings within the system. Only then can we hope to maintain the current level of safety and then move on to find new ways of improving it. We have to devise methods of making the airspace system more user friendly for all categories of flight operations. By constant review of all the information available from technological and other developments, aircrew and supporting personnel will increase knowledge and skills to be better able to manage the machine, which will in turn give a better in-depth awareness of the human weaknesses that jeopardise overall safety, which can only enhance Crew Resource Management techniques; as ICAO circular 240 AN/14L warns: An accident or incident is not solely the result of an action taken by one individual. The potential for an accident is created when human actions and latent failures present within an organisation or the air transport system, interact in a manner which breaches all of the defences.

Summary

From the case study of the F27 disaster we can see that several adverse human attitudes relate to this event.

Risk shifting The co-pilots of both aircraft could have exerted their influence (as part of the crew) to change the outcome of events. Instead, they decided to say nothing, thereby shifting the risk, in effect a resignation by going along with the decisions made by their respective captains. It was under-confidence which led to the acceptance of unreasonable and unsafe actions.

Machismo or 'Rambo' complex Busting weather minimums was obviously something both captains had done before, with the obvious deduction that this was only one in a list of safety violations. This behavioural attitude relates to them having an excessively high opinion of themselves. Indeed it was an effort (by taking risks) to prove to themselves as well as others that they were better than anyone else. Pilots who develop this exaggerated sense of ability (or who submit to undue operational pressure) should not be flying.

Impulsiveness and invulnerability If we take the case of the nineteen-year-old skier as an example, we can see that apart from wanting to prove his manhood, he acted impulsively. He took the incorrect action on the spur of the moment without having time to think through a safer alternative. Being young and already involved in risky sporting activities, he had a feeling of invulnerability. He unconsciously thought that accidents only happened to other people, not himself. Therefore he was prepared to take a considerable risk, ignoring the possibility of a disaster.

The anti-authority 'loose cannon' mentality One of the worst behavioural traits. It stems from feelings of resentment, of being told what we must or must not do. This can lead to ignoring official regulations and procedures. Unfortunately, it can become habitual. If this mentality takes over there is a real danger of sidelining common sense, and in the worst case destroying the ability to make sound decisions. Such behaviour is liable to erupt in a person at any time, and is particularly undesirable in a pilot. It can be triggered if regulations or procedures appear too complicated or restraining.

Complacency It is one of the most insidious problems for a pilot, a sort of 'creeping mental lethargy'. This attitude can quickly lead to a reduced sense of danger if it remains unchecked. Of course it also drastically reduces situational awareness. Complacency often develops in more experienced pilots and starts with confidence, an indispensable pilot trait. Confidence levels are determined by personality, level of training (proficiency) and depth of past experiences. When the (personal, professional) situation stagnates through lack of mental and physical challenge, flying becomes automatic and routine, even boring. This type of complacency is based on passive contentment. The effects start to show with the erosion of proficiency, both on the ground as well as in the air. Professional planning becomes haphazard. Further down the line there could even be physical symptoms such as a weight increase and deterioration in physical condition. This is followed by a loss in personal performance and the ability to self-analyse the situation.

CHAPTER 13
HUMAN FACTORS VERSUS COCKPIT DESIGN

At one time aircraft controls were standard, and so were instrument panel layouts. You could instantly read your indicated airspeed, see the engine RPMs, with the gyro compass telling you your heading. Now it is all changed to a large degree. With new cockpit designs in new-generation aircraft, the future cockpit presentation presents both innovation and challenge to flightcrews.

New pictorial realism

This is one of the most important design principles for the modern cockpit. Instruments, or the electronic displays that represent them, should be as close to the real world as is possible. In other words, we should use easily recognisable and identifiable pictures and symbols rather than something abstract. Simply because an abstract presentation requires an additional mental effort to decipher, we should still use the information it presents.

This new realism has been developed because modern technology (computer presentations in particular) have a large measure of visuality. Scientists tend to convert most abstract words and symbols into graphic images. Then they decide how and in what form they will use them. Therefore, it can be argued that if the original information required in the decision-making process was already presented graphically, no mental gymnastics would be required. One level of interpretation is thus removed. Time is saved and the possibility of errors minimised.

A variety of 'instrumentation' research experiments have been carried out over a number of years, and some interesting results obtained. Let's look at a rather radical example. Words, letters and numbers in all their various forms have traditionally been used in the general human communication process. These can be considered as abstract representations of our thoughts. On an aircraft instrument panel presentation, let's say the bank-angle was provided in digital form (in degrees of bank). On a CRT, left bank was positive, right bank negative, and nil bank zero. The question now is, can the pilot still fly the aircraft on instruments? Research has actually shown that the pilot could do it, but with considerable difficulty. This is the result of using a very experienced professional pilot. In fact what we have is a more positive, easily read display of a conventional attitude instrument (artificial horizon). This allows the pilot to use the indications to control and fly the aircraft. With the advances in CRT pictorial displays, showing attitude, turns, course deviation, etc. all on one instrument (instead of half a dozen), it was even found that individuals with no flying experience at all could manually fly an approach with only half an hour's training. This included DME curves of quite an advanced nature. Most did it as well as a professional pilot.

We cannot apply the principle of pictorial realism right across the board of technology without regard to the objective. We need to consider what we want to achieve – the form of 'message' that makes it readily acceptable and meaningful to the pilot. It is often the case that the 'realistic message' the picture is showing provides far more information than is needed. It may also be disorganised. Some modern flight director systems present so much information (including ILS localiser, glideslope and DME readout), it needs extreme selective concentration to decipher and then use the information required.

To take an everyday example: we can format road maps and city guides any way we want, but the information given must be understandable and above all useable, therefore it doesn't have to have extraneous non-essential detail printed on it. So in the cockpit we need clear presentations that are realistic in giving us the information we need to fly the aircraft. However, computers now have the capability of presenting information in an almost infinite variety of forms. What we use in the cockpit should readily help the pilot in what he needs to know, minimising the possibility of making errors.

Preventing errors in design

Designers have recognised for some time that pilots will make errors in every task in which they are involved. Sometimes the same error may be made by the same pilot just one time. It is certainly true that not every error linked with a particular task will be made by every pilot who attempts it. However, statistics show that a pilot (in a series of pilots) who performs any other particular task will make an error in that operational task. That is human make-up. The first priority of designers should therefore be to design systems that minimise the chances for human error; either that, or make them less susceptible to major failure when an error is made. You notice here we have not said *if*. What this means is that the design can sustain error damage, some form of warning system that checks for the possibility of error occurring, and then warns the pilot before it becomes a full-blown emergency.

Flexibility in the cockpit

To a certain extent there has been some standardisation of automatic systems in the cockpit. But pilots all have some individual style, even within a company's system of standardised operating practices. Styles are based on where and how a pilot was trained, as well as the individual personality. It is widely thought that in future cockpits pilots will have the choice of electronic displays and automated systems that will be compatible with their own style. No one has yet considered how this might fit in with standardisation as we know it now.

In the future, it has also been suggested that designers need to introduce computers which will monitor a pilot's cognitive functions, meaning, I suppose, that the computer's memory will be programmed with a whole range of pilot intention scenarios based on a predetermined range of how a pilot behaves in a series of operational situations. The computer can then compare the pilot's behaviour, or cognitive decision-making, with a pre-evaluated range of proved good decisions.

Coping with systems failure

A pilot expects that if a technical system fails the aircraft will not fall out of the sky. The designers will have built in a back-up system to take care of the immediate problem so as to avoid a major problem. Technical failures of any sort are unwelcome, as they increase the pilot's task loading in the cockpit. This is a particular concern to aircrew of the new generation 'fly-by-wire' aircraft. Eventually this technology will filter through to the general aviation sector of the industry. At that stage it is hoped that scientists will have perfected automatic back-up system failure switch-over, which will take care of the 'failing' system in three different stages according to the function and importance of the system:

1. *Complete failure*: The primary system function is taken over automatically by a back-up and maintains integrity and performance. The pilot need take no action, other than note it has happened.
2. *Complete failure*: The primary system failure is backed up by the manual switch-over initiated and carried out by the pilot. It is a simple exercise and there is little change in the pilot's cockpit task loading.
3. *Complete failure – fail-safe*: The back-up for the primary system is entirely manual and initiated by the pilot. There is some additional pilot task loading, but it is not excessive.

New techniques in automatic, computer-controlled aircraft systems are, in reality, only in their early stages, perhaps more so in military than civil aircraft.

These computer systems will probably be so sophisticated that they will replace some aircrew in the future, particularly the 'back-seater', nav-systems operator in some military fighters.

This chapter only gives a brief insight into the new technology of the future. No one can really do more than that. We can only speculate that technical failures of all sorts of systems – secondary displays, alarms, even controls – will conceivably be fail-automatic back-up, fail-safe automatic or manual back-up. What we have to watch out for is that future designs promote real improvements the pilots can live with, reducing the risk of errors. To do that, though, human factors versus technology has to be closely monitored.

CHAPTER 14

HUMAN CAPABILITIES VERSUS COCKPIT DESIGN

To understand how cockpit design is developed in relation to human capabilities, we have to find out what tasks aircrew are good at, including those that do not readily fit into the human equation. First of all, we have to look at the mental information-gathering process, which is divided into four parts:

- Basic information-gathering
- Information processing and evaluation
- Making considered decisions
- Practical action

The information is essential to all levels of design personnel, because it helps them decide how the human element fits into the machine (aircraft).

Pilot information

The pilot needs to have all the relevant technical and operational performance data so that the aircraft can be used safely. It needs to be presented in a way that is easily and quickly understood, so that decisions can be made without undue complications. Research has shown that humans are much better than machines in several areas: interpreting visual and aural information; recognising changes in sounds and pictures, or variations in more complex patterns; and in the anticipation of flight events which may compromise the safety of the flight. Machines, however, can better detect (because of technology) radio signals of various types and radar emissions. This is obviously outside human capability anyway.

The machine can also quite successfully monitor itself in terms of engine parameters, fuel consumption, etc., with the human element monitoring the machine to detect irregularities and action accordingly. The machine only does that in specific circumstances (autofeather is one example). Collision avoidance is the responsibility of the pilots and not a design consideration. Having said that, electronic proximity-alerting systems such as GWPS and TCAS are being increasingly used. Whereas machines can instantly detect variations in performance without any divided attention indefinitely, human attention is soon divided or distracted through boredom or fatigue. For some time there has been discussion about a fully automated aircraft without pilots for the future. However, there are overwhelming reasons for retaining pilots on the flight deck. On a fully automated computer-controlled aircraft, if some serious technical problem developed, the human pilot would be able to cope with the problem more easily than the computer. It is better design policy to keep the pilot flying the aircraft, and let the computers monitor performance. From a safety point of view the human pilot is always in the technical-operational loop, and has direct control of all the systems. Then if (because of human fallibility) pilot attention lags, the computer can prompt.

Information-processing by the pilot

A great deal of technical information is presented to the pilot by the machine. The pilot deals with this *selectively* as required during all stages of the flight. The human element only has a certain level of capabilities at performing particular tasks when compared to the machine. We can analyse the difference between the human and machine capabilities, which is directly related to the level of complexity.

Humans:

- can remember principles better than facts (which can help in decision-making)
- can build up a whole range of general information over a long period (long-term memory capability)
- are good at sifting through information and reaching decisions
- are good at exercising judgement and allocating tasks

Machines:

- can better store information and retrieve it quickly
- are good at doing complicated computations and generating solutions (deductive reasoning)

This input is through selected information banks compiled from human resources.

In such a complex machine environment, it is important that pilots should not be compelled to remember too much detailed information. This is why checklists are so essential. The pilot is also bombarded with a range of other information that has to be written down, because it would be almost impossible to remember it accurately. This mainly comes through air traffic control.

Pilot decision-making

Decision-making is part of information-processing. It involves elements of judgement and how the individual perceives the data presented. This is certainly one area where humans are better than machines. The capability of humans is better in the problem-solving process when the outcome is uncertain. Machines cannot place values on different decisions – humans can. These values are therefore used to make a final choice.

Actioning decisions

There is no doubt that machines always out-perform humans in the aviation operational environment. The question then arises, if a machine (being the whole range of computers) can out-perform a human (pilot), but a pilot is an essential part of the flight equation, how can the aircraft designer involve both? We have seen that the pilot needs to be involved to deal with any emergency with which the machine cannot cope. What aircraft designers seem to have decided on is only having a 'partly automatic' aircraft. By following this 'technical path', the pilot plays an essential part in flying the aircraft, but the computers perform as many of the control tasks as possible. This operational (design) decision is based on the technical fact that computers can indeed fly better (more smoothly and economically) than a pilot. The problem arises when there is a serious fault (engine, equipment). There is then a scramble between human and machine to take over and overcome it.

Human factors and pilot error

You might well ask what this has to do with cockpit design. To answer that we have to define exactly what these two elements really are.

Let us take human factors (HF) first. Pilot performance (the way the pilot operates in the cockpit) is influenced by basic design (accessibility of controls and systems), how the body organs function, the influence of emotions and interaction with other aircrew and aviation personnel. This includes ground staff (engineering, operations, traffic and ATC).

As we know that pilot error is the major cause in the majority of aircraft accidents, we need to know exactly what is meant by pilot error. Pilot error is defined as an action or decision that is made by the pilot that might contribute to an accident (or incident) if left uncorrected. This includes indecision or simply doing nothing.

Pilot error does not actually mean that all errors are the fault of the pilot, because it is possible outside factors are the cause. This could relate to poor cockpit design – the position of controls or badly placed instruments.

Statistics show us that around 80% of accidents in GA are caused by pilot error, although not because of major malfunctions in aircraft systems. There is no doubt most major accidents would never have taken place had the pilots taken the necessary corrective actions.

Furthermore, accident experts believe that pilots are not trained to handle many of the internal and external forces which affect them. Most are not even aware of their existence. In the real world of flying, there are many confusing and often misleading things that can happen to a pilot in the cockpit, sensory illusions being one of them. In IFR check-outs, when handling unusual attitudes, I've seen very experienced pilots become confused between what their vestibular senses are telling them and what the various instruments are showing. This problem leads to loss of control of the aircraft. It is a human factor and relates directly to flying ability. The error that took place shows the pilot has been presented with the correct information, but the brain has incorrectly interpreted it, which gives rise to an error in the decision-making process. Like everything else relating to pilot proficiency, performance can be improved through additional or revised knowledge and training.

From this we see that when these factors adversely affect the pilot he/she may well perform so badly it can result in an accident. What this means is, the responsibility for accidents is mostly the fault of the human element in the aircraft, not the machine itself. The most common causes of accidents are:

- loss of directional control
- poor judgement by the pilot
- airspeed not maintained
- poor *pre-flight* planning and decision-making
- ATC clearance not maintained
- inadvertent stall (loss of aircraft control)
- handling the aircraft badly in a crosswind
- poor *in-flight* planning and decision-making

If we analyse each and every one they are the result of poor to bad pilot performance, meaning proficiency. They are not part of any aircraft equipment faults.

Pilot performance

Information flows to the pilot via several sources. The majority of this comes through sight and hearing. Smell and touch also play a large part.

There are two problems that can occur at this first stage: the information may be incorrect, confused or remain undetected; or the correct information is available but the brain misinterprets it. In both these cases, the brain's decision-making process uses incorrect information. Therefore the brain will obviously make a poor, less effective decision using less than accurate information.

A number of aspects are important when we consider the processing of available information by the brain:

- the ability of the brain and its awareness in noticing this data
- the ability to disseminate multiple pieces of information reaching the brain all at the same time
- the ability to focus in and choose between relevant and non-relevant information

The brain must also be able to change rapidly between selected tasks that must be dealt with simultaneously, if necessary to prioritise them. This can include flying and controlling the aircraft, as well as coping with an in-flight emergency. The problem is that at this stage errors can occur. The brain can be concentrating so much on one task, it ignores incoming information from another.

Pilots are susceptible to another common error. They often fail to decide on the best data, or cross-check the accuracy of information from another source. The brain can also be so fully occupied on one task it excludes everything else.

The final decision-making process

We can say this is part of information-processing, but distractions can and do occur. Even if accurate information is being used by the brain, the quality of the decision can be greatly influenced by social, emotional, domestic pressures, even lack of oxygen (hypoxia).

The implementation of decisions

Problems can still occur, even if accurate decisions have been made. Factors that do not allow the pilot to act can creep in. Fatigue is one, stress is another. If the pilot is physically below par this can also have a decidedly adverse effect. The old hot potato in multi-crew operations is poor communications between crew members. There are numerous documented examples where relevant technical information has not been shared, or ignored by individual crew members, which has resulted in an accident.

Summary

- errors can creep into the decision-making process at a number of stages
- errors can be caused by faulty information, or faulty interpretation of accurate information
- even if accurate information is available to the brain (as the primary processor), the brain itself may introduce errors: by ignoring accurate data; by not noticing data at all; by failing to cope with all the tasks requiring attention; by not properly considering all the alternative courses of action; or as a result of external pressures influencing the pilot to choose a poor alternative
- errors can even happen when the correct decision has been made – the pilot may be in a physical or mental state that prevents or hinders the ability to perform proficiently.

CHAPTER 15

DISTRACTIONS IN THE COCKPIT ENVIRONMENT

A distraction is 'that which draws the sight, mind or attention to a different object or, confusingly, attracts in different directions at once'. It can compromise flight safety in two ways:

- failure to accomplish an essential task (e.g. not watching out for conflicting traffic, which results in a near-miss incident)
- crew co-ordination or cockpit management functions interrupted or bypassed – the loss of organised crew teamwork leads to inattention, resulting in deviations from the desired flight path

An analysis of distraction causes revealed that priorities for routine cockpit tasks followed rather consistent patterns:

- during excessive workload, checklists were always accomplished, radar was monitored and minor malfunctions handled
- routine traffic watch and air traffic communications (particularly at tower hand-off) were lower-priority items, and sometimes not accomplished in time to avoid an unsafe condition
- when radar advised there was specific conflict with other traffic, the crew made identification and (if necessary) course changes the highest priority; this often caused lapses in cockpit management and crew co-ordination

General

In a US NBAA report following an extensive review of cockpit distractions there were thirteen distractions due to studying approach plates or terminal area charts: nine altitude deviations (mostly overshoots); three near misses; and one route deviation from the 'read as you fly' technique. One significant factor that came to light was that twelve of the thirteen distractions in the first item occurred below 11,000 feet. There is an inference that complacency may have interfered with adequate pre-planning. In one particular incident, a pilot used an out-of-date chart during profile descent, while the other pilot actually reviewed the wrong approach procedure. (It should be pointed out that distraction through approach plate/chart review does not tend to combine with other tasks, and is seldom a function of cockpit workload. It appears to be a momentary lapse in cockpit management and crew co-ordination.)

The crew

- inexperienced co-pilots may add to the cockpit workload and disturb the normal cockpit management function
- monitoring or instructing a new co-pilot may distract the captain from performing normal duties
- a captain may be occupied in a routine task and miss mistakes due to inexperience or unfamiliarity with the route, equipment and procedures.

There were found to be ten distraction events associated with crew fatigue. Although fatigue itself is not a distraction, it increases the pilot's vulnerability to distractions. The results were: six altitude deviations; one approach to the wrong airport; two route deviations; and one misread chart. (Note: The work–rest cycle is highlighted by such comments as 'seventh approach today', 'on duty seven days in a row', 'eight landings with three instrument approaches in thunderstorm activity'.)

Conclusions

The study was dominated by the frequency of one phrase: 'we were distracted by'. In many cases the sentence was completed by the mention of any ordinary cockpit task. Pilots recognised that distraction meant attention was diverted from management of the cockpit and aircraft, especially in relation to the desired flight path. There has been a general lack of understanding that on a particular flight and specific time (referring to *any* of the flights studied), accomplishing the usual cockpit tasks suddenly and unexpectedly ended in near disaster.

In all the findings, distraction as a human factor cannot in any circumstances be eliminated from the cockpit. However, the identification and type classification of distraction incidents suggest possible improved techniques for minimising distraction causes. This is very important because distraction is not merely a cause of individual error. More critically, it impairs crew concept fundamentals which have been 'human-engineered' to protect against the errors crew members will inevitably commit.

Avoid the 'guessing game'

Effects of distraction could easily be diminished if pilots were cautioned in their early 'guessing' as to the altitude clearance attitude to be received. Pre-take-off selection of an ATC altitude that results in mis-setting the correct altitude reminder is linked with distraction resulting in altitude overshoots. (The added trap in this error is that a lower altitude restriction is usually due to traffic at the normally expected level. Although the convention is that one pilot flies the aircraft, the distinction may become obscured when the aircraft is under control of the autopilot. Both pilots tend to become vulnerable to *any* distraction. Therefore auto-capture of level-off must be monitored.)

Special recommendations

Airlines, as well as general aviation and corporate aircraft flight standards, should ensure that crew co-ordination principles are applied in such 'real-life' on-line distractions as weather avoidance, radar monitoring, and minor system abnormalities during the climb and descent phases of flight. Distraction is most critical at ground level to 3,000 feet, the 10,000 to 11,000 feet level, plus 500 feet altitudes occupied by VFR traffic skirting the edges of controlled terminal area airspace.

The distraction due to workload could be reduced and cockpit vigilance increased, particularly if low-altitude level-off restrictions and heading changes could be minimised during SID climb-outs. Noise abatement procedures may increase cockpit workload by requiring precision flying during power reductions, airspeed changes, sharp turns, plus altitude and aircraft configuration changes.

CHAPTER 16

THE AUTOMATIC COMPLACENCY VERSUS COCKPIT SAFETY

Using autothrottle has the tendency to degrade speed consciousness. Likewise, altitude preselect reduces our height consciousness, and the autopilot takes over the pilot's function of physically flying the aircraft.

We can see from this that an increasing amount of technology does a significant part of the pilot's work automatically, except that it does not always do it intelligently. So if we have an interface problem between the individual systems we most certainly have a problem. If we progress this one step further, we are faced with what can only be described as a man and machine interface problem.

Let's look at the autothrottle and the autopilot. They normally perform their functions very well, but neither system knows much about what the other is doing, or indeed plans to. And either system is even less knowledgeable about operational limitations (with a few exceptions). In spite of everything, we still seem to rely on automatic systems, in this case automatic flight control. We do this to such a degree that it is easy to let our attention wander away from the primary flight instruments. It could also be that we neglect to take care of essential cockpit priorities.

To get to grips with the problems, we should keep in our mind that machines, however technologically complex, are only tools to aid the flightcrew in performing a variety of specific cockpit tasks. What we have to grasp is the fact that machines cannot think for us. They cannot work or function outside their own designed limitations, or be complacent – only man can be that. Machines should not be left to their own devices by man without knowing their faults, or their capabilities and limitations.

Examples of 'automation' machine problems

– taken from actual incident reports

- The altitude preselect malfunctioned during descent. The problem went unnoticed by the flightcrew and an excessive undershoot resulted.
- During a final approach the autothrottle became unserviceable. The speed dropped fifteen knots below the correct target speed before the malfunction was noticed.

- During levelling off with the altitude preselect (throttles at flight idle), the speed dropped close to the stall before it was noticed and rectified by applying power.
- In *en route* navigation mode, the aircraft turned the wrong way over a waypoint. Although this was noticed immediately, the command pilot did not take any corrective action until the aircraft had turned more than 45°.
- During an automatic ILS approach, a bend in the glideslope caused the aircraft to adopt a marked pitch-down attitude. This immediately resulted in an excessive sink rate. Although the pilot was fully aware of what was happening, he did not react until the situation was so critical that a very low pull-up had to be made.

These are just a few samples from many reports of a similar kind. This highlights the disfunction between man and machine – the interface problem – brought about when the normal routine breaks down. The disturbing element is that man has a tendency to defend himself by blaming the technology, which is only one part of the factor. It follows therefore that there has been a break in the management of cockpit resources by the crew. When in doubt *think basic* and trust the basic instruments to tell you what the aircraft is doing (the instrument-scanning routine).

Know and understand the realities

The machine does not relieve man of his responsibilities, and it is a false illusion to assume that it reduces the workload significantly in achieving the expected goals. What the machine actually does is increase the total capacity, which:

- balances the workload
- improves accuracy
- improves safety
- reduces costs
- improves regularity

In this technologically advancing world, the pilot's managing role in the man–machine interface can be summarised into a logical series of actions:

- *plan* how the machines can be used in the overall flight context
- *programme* them for the task(s) in hand
- *confirm* the overall objectives
- *monitor* performance
- *identify* and *correct* faults
- *reject* and *revise* as and if necessary

Working *with* the machines and using them to the best advantage, taking into account all the various factors, is a safe way forward. To summarise:

- be aware of the automatic system limitations
- don't change your normal (cockpit) piloting priorities
- be absolutely clear at the outset what the system is supposed to do and what its limitations are
- be wary of any anomalies in the system(s)
- monitor and check what each system is doing (good management of cockpit resources)
- don't hesitate to reject a system if you have any doubts about its accuracy
- don't accept an automated system performance that under any specific circumstance you as the pilot can do better – and more safely.

Try to use and interface with your automated systems in the best way you know how, and to *your* advantage. The machine is there to serve you. All this will help to alleviate the automatic complacency syndrome.

CHAPTER 17
FLIGHT PHYSIOLOGY

Composition of the air

The earth is surrounded by layers of gases, particles of matter and water vapour. This mixture is called air; collectively the layers are the atmosphere, which is held by gravity around the earth.

This large volume of air has considerable weight at the earth's surface, and is approximately 15lb per square inch, or 30in. of mercury. In the lower layers of the atmosphere the relative proportions of each gas stay reasonably constant, the most abundant of which is nitrogen at 78% and oxygen, 21%. Other gases make up the remaining one per cent. Carbon dioxide accounts for only 0.03%, but it is vital to life since plants need it for photosynthesis. The atmosphere also contains solid particles, including dust. Condensation of moisture is thought to occur on these particles, which are considered important to the development of certain types of weather, like clouds, mist and fog.

All aircrew should understand the chemical and physical structure of the atmosphere. We are aware oxygen is necessary to sustain human life by oxidising the food we eat to produce heat and energy. The physical properties of the atmosphere, being temperature, humidity and density, are equally important to the pilot because of meteorology as well as their effect on human performance.

The atmosphere is divided into layers, each having different characteristics. As pilots we will probably never go beyond the first layer, the troposphere, which extends upwards from the surface to around 50,000 feet. This upper level depends on a variety of conditions. On top of this is a thin layer called the tropopause, which confines most of the water vapour.

The method of determining air density is by measuring the pressure of the atmosphere; in other words, the weight of the air per unit area. Instead of the measurement being converted directly into pounds per square inch (or kilograms per square centimetre), it is usual to measure pressure in terms of how tall a column of mercury the atmosphere can support. The standard measurement is in millibars, also called hectopascals. In North America, inches of mercury is used.

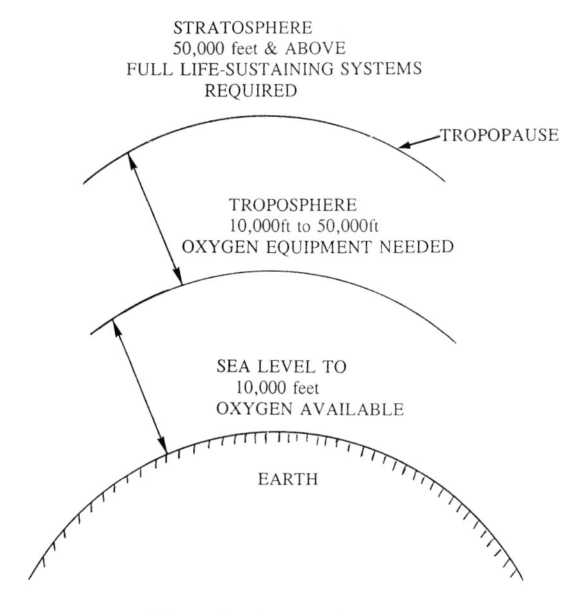

Figure 9 Atmosphere layers

The physical gas laws

Pilots need to have a basic knowledge of the physical gas laws in view of their relationship to a number of physiological problems that can be encountered during flight. We know that air is a mixture of gases which are compressible, but they are subject to certain established laws governing reaction to changes in pressure, temperature, volume and density. The two best-known laws are worth noting here; they are Boyle's Law and Charles's Law.

BOYLE'S LAW states that providing the temperature is constant the volume of a gas is inversely proportional to its pressure. This basically means that when the pressure increases the volume decreases, and when the pressure decreases the volume increases. If we consider it another way, we can say that at a fixed temperature the pressure of the gas varies inversely with its volume. But Boyle's Law is exactly correct only at moderate temperatures, being more approximate at extremes of temperature. It also explains some of the altitude effects on the gas-containing cavities of the human body during flight. As altitude increases the gas within the middle ear, sinuses, stomach and intestines will expand. Sometimes this can be very painful and can cause severe discomfort.

CHARLES'S LAW states that the volume of a fixed mass of gas held at a constant pressure varies directly with the absolute temperature. One feature of gas expansion is that equal volumes of different gases expand by the same amount when heated at the same temperature. So provided the pressure remains constant, each degree centigrade rise in temperature will cause the gases to expand by $\frac{1}{273}$ of the volume they would occupy at 0°C. An alternate way of stating this law is: The volume of a fixed mass of gas at constant pressure is directly proportional to its absolute temperature.

Both Boyle's and Charles's gas laws can be summarised by the equation: $\frac{pv}{T}$ = a constant, where p = pressure, v = volume, and T = absolute temperature. This gas equation applies even when there is a change in all three variables of pressure, volume and temperature.

The air, oxygen requirements and availability

We are aware that the air surrounding the earth is supporting the weight of air above it, and its molecules will therefore be pressed close together, causing the density of the air to be greatest at the surface. At sea level a normal healthy person can extract enough oxygen from the air to pursue normal activities. Above 8,000 feet, however, the effects of lack of oxygen remain very much the same up to a very high altitude. The reduction in the pressure of the atmosphere has a significant effect on the partial pressure exerted by the oxygen.

The amount of oxygen consumed by the human body during the respiratory cycle depends primarily upon the degree of physical or mental activity of the individual. A person walking at a brisk pace will consume about four times as much oxygen as when resting. In the course of an average day, a normal adult will consume about two and a half pounds of oxygen. This is approximately equivalent to the normal average weight of food consumed daily. An oxygen supply which might be adequate for a person at rest would not be enough for the same individual when flying under severe weather conditions or when under mental stress.

Oxygen becomes more difficult to obtain as the altitude increases. This is because the air becomes less and less dense and there is a decrease in the total pressure. As the total pressure decreases, so does the pressure of oxygen, even though the percentage of oxygen in the air remains constant. For example, at 40,000 feet, the total pressure is only 2.7 p.s.i., and the oxygen pressure is 0.56 p.s.i. Just to understand how quickly air pressure, and thus density, decreases with altitude, refer to Fig. 10, Altitude and pressure table. At about 18,000 feet (around 5,490 metres), the air is half as dense as it is at sea level.

ALTITUDE		PRESSURE		
Feet	Metres	Inches (Hg)	Millibars	Millimetres (Hg)
0	0	29.92	1,013.25	760.0
3,000	910	26.82	908.2	681.2
6,000	1,830	23.98	812.1	609.1
9,000	2,740	21.39	724.3	543.3
12,000	3,660	19.04	644.6	483.6
15,000	4,570	16.89	572.1	429.0
18,000	5,490	14.95	506.3	379.7
21,000	6,400	13.19	446.8	335.0
24,000	7,320	11.61	393.2	294.9

Figure 10 Altitude and pressure table

As altitude increases and the pressure of oxygen is reduced, the amount of oxygen transfer in the lung air sacs is reduced, resulting in a decrease in the percentage of oxygen saturation in the blood. This causes a deficiency of oxygen throughout the body. For this reason, supplemental oxygen, pressurised cabins and, in certain (military) aircraft, pressure suits are required if the body is to receive adequate oxygen.

The total effect on an oxygen-deprived person is the result of both altitude and time of exposure. Every cell in the body is affected by the lack of oxygen, but the primary effects are on the brain and the nervous system. Above 10,000 feet, deterioration of both physical and mental performance is a gradually progressive condition. Impairment can soon become severe with increase in altitude and prolonged exposure. The effect of lack of oxygen in the body is called hypoxia. The following list highlights the most common symptoms:

- increased breathing rate
- light-headed or dizzy sensation
- tingling or warm sensation
- sweating
- reduced visual field
- sleepiness
- blue colouring of skin, fingernails and lips
- behavioural changes

Subtle hypoxic effects may be noticeable at 5,000 feet at night. In the average individual, night vision will be blurred and narrowed. Also dark adaptation will be affected. At 8,000 feet night vision is reduced by as much as 25% without supplemental oxygen. Few or no effects will be noticed during daylight at these altitudes.

As there are different ways such oxygen deprivation can occur, hypoxia takes on different forms:

Hypoxic hypoxia This happens when there is insufficient oxygen in the lungs for proper transfer to take place, or when the lungs do not transfer the available oxygen efficiently. In a pilot, the most common cause is being at too high an altitude without supplemental oxygen.

Anaemic hypoxia Caused when the blood's capacity to carry oxygen is impaired. There might be sufficient oxygen in the lungs, but the blood has lost some of its capacity to carry it, for instance if an individual is anaemic and has a lack of blood cells, or after donating blood. The most common cause in aviation occurs from carbon monoxide poisoning. In small amounts there is an impairment of brain functions and sight; in larger amounts it causes death.

Stagnant hypoxia In pilots this rarely occurs. There might be the correct amount of oxygen in the blood, but the blood pools and circulation is below normal. The condition can be brought on by the high g-forces that occur in aerobatics.

Histotoxic hypoxia Caused by the body's inability to take the oxygen it needs from the blood. The blood might well have the correct amount of oxygen and be circulating efficiently, but the body's cells have lost their ability to extract the necessary oxygen. Symptoms can easily occur under the influence of alcohol or drugs, and in a person suffering from cyanide poisoning.

In every one of the cases outlined here the net effect is the same: reduced oxygen throughout the body, but most importantly to the brain and eyes.

The effect of hypoxia varies between individuals, but there is a common denominator in measuring the effects of hypoxia using a time and altitude table for the time of useful consciousness (TUC). This is the time you have to continue to perform tasks in a reasonably competent manner without the use of supplemental oxygen (Fig. 11).

As we see from the reference table, as altitude increases, your ability to perform rapidly declines.

Oxygen systems

Oxygen systems are generally matched to aircraft performance. The continuous flow system, which is effective up to 25,000 feet, is mostly used in general aviation aircraft. For altitudes up to 35,000 feet, a diluter-demand system is avail-

Altitude feet	metres	While sitting quietly	During moderate activity
40,000	12,200	30 sec	18 sec
35,000	10,670	45 sec	30 sec
30,000	9,140	1.15 min	45 sec
25,000	7,620	3 min	2 min
22,000	6,710	10 min	5 min
20,000	6,100	12 min	5 min
18,000	5,490	30 min	20 min

Figure 11 Time of useful consciousness table

able. The pressure-demand system is used for altitudes up to 45,000 feet where high-performance jet aircraft operate.

Continuous flow system

The continuous flow system is the simplest in design and operation. This is characterised by the continuous delivery of 100% oxygen whenever a mask is plugged in. These systems consist of four main components: high-pressure storage cylinder; regulator; distribution system; and continuous flow masks.

Diluter-demand system

In contrast to the continuous flow system, the diluter-demand type supplies oxygen to the user only when it is inhaled. The diluter-demand mask is shown in Fig. 12. The mixture of oxygen and air is regulated automatically up to 30,000 feet. At this point the system begins to deliver 100% oxygen. It can be used with safety up to 35,000 feet.

Pressure-demand system

The pressure-demand system varies from the diluter-demand system in one particular respect. Above 30,000 feet, oxygen is delivered to the mask under positive pressure in order to maintain proper blood oxygen saturation. However, because of this pressure, exhaling and talking are difficult and need practice. The air-tight mask is especially important with this system.

Safety tips concerning oxygen

Gaseous oxygen is chemically stable and is non-flammable. Nevertheless, combustible materials ignite more rapidly and burn with greater intensity in

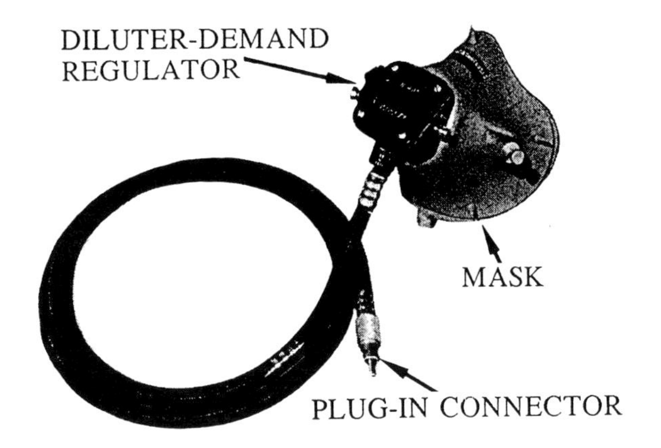

Figure 12 Diluter-demand mask

an oxygen-rich atmosphere. In addition, oxygen combines with oil, grease or bituminous material to form a highly explosive mixture which is sensitive to impact. Physical damage to or failure of oxygen containers, valves or associated plumbing can result in explosive rupture, with danger to life and surrounding property.

Hyperventilation

This is a form used to describe breathing that is too fast and too deep. It results in an excess of oxygen and a deficiency of carbon dioxide (one of the triggers for breathing). Hyperventilation usually occurs involuntarily as a response to a stressful situation. It has symptoms that are often mistaken for hypoxia: dizziness, tingling of the fingers and toes, muscle spasms, increased sensation of body heat, nausea, rapid heart rate, blurred vision, and, finally, loss of consciousness. This condition can quickly be rectified, and an individual brought back to a normal breathing pattern. It can be done by a conscious lowering of the breathing rate, or by engaging the person in ordinary conversation, thus diverting attention from the stress. Breathing slowly in and out of a paper bag also helps because it increases the carbon dioxide in the lungs.

Vertigo

During day-to-day activities, the ability of the human body to function correctly and precisely depends partly upon a person's ability accurately to determine his position relative to the earth. This ability to orient himself correctly is especially important to the pilot. The sensations from several sources are used to maintain balance: the eyes, the nerve endings in the muscles and about the joints, and certain tiny balance organs which are part of the inner ear structure.

A pilot who has entered clouds and can no longer perceive ground references literally will not be able to tell 'which end is up' from his balance organs' signals. This happens because these nerve endings and balance organs depend, for the most part, upon a correct orientation to the pull of gravity, and yet these forces may not be oriented in the same direction as gravity. The brain struggles to decipher signals sent from the senses, but without the clue normally supplied by vision incorrect or conflicting interpretations may result. The result of such sensory confusion is a dizzy, whirling sensation termed 'vertigo', sometimes referred to as 'spatial disorientation'.

Vertigo may take a variety of forms and may be produced by a number of different flight situations in IFR *and* VFR conditions. For example, a pilot conducting a night flight above an inclined cloud layer which is well illuminated by moonlight might experience sensory confusion. The reason for this confusion is that most people naturally assume a cloud layer to be parallel to the surface of the earth. However, if the cloud layer is inclined, the pilot might attempt to align the aircraft with the cloud layer, thereby creating a wing-low attitude or gradually increasing rate of climb or descent. In turbulence, if an aircraft is rolled abruptly right or left, then slowly resumes straight-and-level flight, the pilot may be aware of the roll, but not the recovery. On the other hand, if the aircraft rolls very slowly to the left, the pilot might still believe the aircraft to be in straight-and-level flight. A pitch change of 20° from the horizontal, if done slowly and without visual reference, may go unnoticed. Also, in a banked turn, centrifugal force tends to press the body into the seat, much the same as when the aircraft is entering a climb or levelling off from a descent. Without visual reference, a banked turn may be interpreted as a climb. When completing a turn, the reduction in pressure gives the pilot the same sensation as going into a dive, and may be interpreted this way.

Flicker vertigo

There are other special causes of vertigo in addition to spatial disorientation (balance organ confusion); among them is the effect of a flickering light or shadow at a constant frequency. Flicker vertigo can result from a light flickering fourteen to twenty times a second and may produce unpleasant and dangerous reactions in some persons. These reactions include dizziness, nausea, disorientation and unconsciousness. They are especially insidious because the subject is often not aware of the cause of distress.

In a single-engine aircraft flying toward the sun, the propeller can cause a vertigo-producing flickering effect, especially when the engine is throttled back for a landing approach. The flickering shadows of helicopter blades have been known to cause flicker vertigo, as has the bounce-back from rotating beacons or strobe lights when operated in or near the clouds at night. Pilots operating under instrument conditions are advised to turn off the rotating beacon or strobe lights in order to avoid this effect. Slight changes in propeller or rotor r.p.m. will usually produce relief when the effect cannot be otherwise avoided.

Illusions during instrument flight conditions

A very serious but common type of sensory illusion may occur when a non-instrument-rated pilot continues flight into instrument conditions. When this occurs, the pilot has lost outside visual reference. Often the aircraft will enter a very slight bank at a rate undetectable to the sense of balance. This bank will generally increase until there is a noticeable loss of altitude. The pilot, noting the decrease in altitude and still believing that he is in level flight, may apply elevator back pressure and perhaps add power in an attempt to recover the lost altitude. This manoeuvre only serves to tighten the spiral, unless he has the presence of mind first to correct the bank attitude of the aircraft.

Once the spiral has started, the pilot will suffer an illusion of turning in the opposite direction if he tries to stop the turning motion of the aircraft. Under these circumstances, it is unlikely that he will take the appropriate corrective action. Rather, he will continue tightening the spiral. In these circumstances a dangerous situation can quickly develop. This unfortunate situation all too often occurs to pilots without instrument training who mistakenly believe that they can maintain their orientation in clouds.

Stars and ground lights

A common problem associated with night flying is the confusion of ground lights with stars. Many incidents are recorded in which pilots have put their aircraft into very unusual attitudes in order to keep ground lights above them, having mistaken them for stars. Some pilots have misinterpreted the lights along the seashore as the horizon, and have manoeuvred their aircraft dangerously close to the sea while under the impression that they were flying straight and level.

Visual illusions

This is an area of vision that can and does cause the greatest concern for a pilot. It carries a high potential risk for an inexperienced or unwary pilot. The problem lies in the fact that there are many normal situations that the pilot can easily misinterpret because of the type of visual information received by the eyes, then processed by the brain.

Illusion of the black hole

The black hole illusion has been blamed as the possible cause of several aviation accidents. This can occur during a night approach over ground without any lights. It can easily take place over water. What happens is, the dark area in the foreground causes bright (high intensity) approach and runway lighting in the far to middle distance to appear to be lower than they really are, which gives the illusion of being higher. Any increase in the aircraft rate of descent in this situation could lead to a disastrous accident.

Visual illusions are concisely summarised below. These are the main types of illusion that can be encountered, and the result.

Runway approach illusions

Runway	Illusion	Result
Upsloping Runway	Shows Greater Height	Lower Approaches
Narrower Runway	Shows Greater Height	Lower Approaches
Featureless Terrain	Shows Greater Height	Lower Approaches
Downsloping Runway	Shows Lower Height	Higher Approaches
Wider Runway	Shows Lower Height	Higher Approaches
Bright Runway and Approach Lights	Shorter Distance	Higher Approaches

CHAPTER 18
VISION IN FLIGHT

All flightcrew must have extremely good eyesight to operate an aircraft safely. Of the five senses that a pilot uses, vision is relied on more than any other. Of course there are limitations with which aircrew should be familiar. Good vision is required in depth perception, particularly during the landing phase to judge the final approach and flare-out. There is also the requirement to avoid obstructions, judge distances, read maps, charts and instruments. As a pilot ages there will be some defects in vision, but usually this can be corrected with spectacles. Like every other subject about which a pilot should have knowledge, vision is no exception. The pilot must have an understanding of the principles relating to the eye to obtain the best results.

Anatomy of the eye

The eye is somewhat like a camera. It is similar in design, having a shutter, diaphragm, lens and a mechanism for focusing. The eyeball itself is moved by the muscles that surround it, and the fluid (tears) that moistens the cornea is produced by the lachrymal gland. The eyelids act as shutters for the eyeballs. Light passes through the cornea before reaching the lens. In conditions of reduced light the pupil grows larger (this is very apparent in cats), and decreases as the light grows stronger. This allows the correct amount of light to fall on the retina. The lens focuses the light on the retina (see Fig. 13).

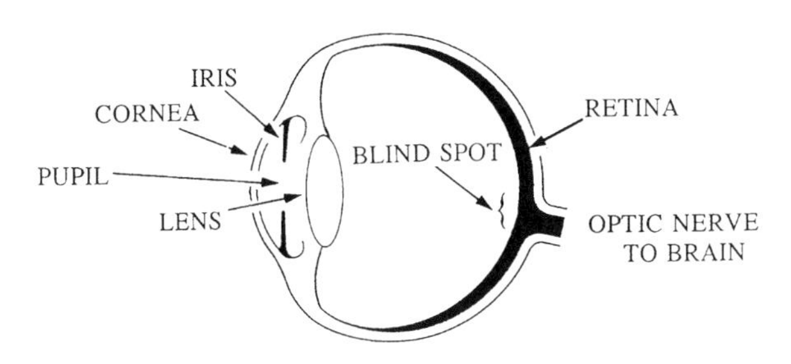

Figure 13 Main parts of the eye

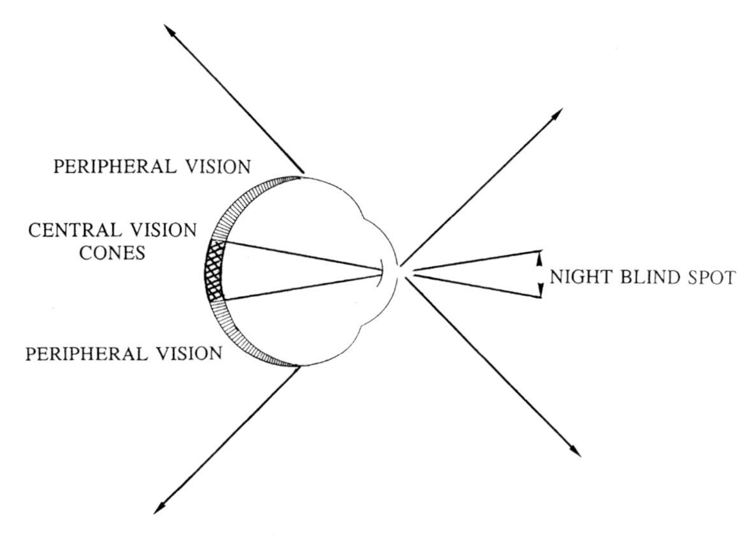

Figure 14 Vision limits

Physiology relating to vision

The retina has (special cell) receptors which convert light energy into nerve impulses, which pass other cells in the retina before travelling along to the optic nerve, then to the optic chiasma. (This is the crossroads, as it were, of the two nerve tracts leading to each side of the brain. The brain has an area known as the visual cortex where information from both eyes is interpreted.) There are two types of nerve endings in the retina which can be identified by their construction and function. The small central area of the retina is largely composed of nerve endings called cones, which can detect fine detail. However, there are very small multiple nerve endings differentiated by their construction and function. They are a measure of central vision and are needed for maximum visual acuity, and for differentiating colour. One disadvantage of cones is that they function poorly in dim light.

Acuity measures the ability to perceive the shape and actual detail of objects. Aircrew must meet minimum standards of visual acuity established with a standard test card or something similar. Some common defects can be optically corrected so that aircrew can meet the minimum required standards.

Regardless of other problems, clarity of vision will be affected by:

- the size and shape of objects
- the available light
- the distance from the eye

- the actual visibility
- how the surroundings affect the object being viewed
- whether the object is moving

Visual acuity is better through central vision and gets worse towards the edge of the retina. Because of this objects within the entire field of vision are not seen with the same sharpness. In fact just a short distance each side of the central vision field, acuity reduces considerably; therefore objects are best seen when we look directly at them. For a pilot when scanning the sky for other aircraft, it is better to use short movements of both eye and head, thus dividing the sky into sections. An aircraft that falls within peripheral vision can be seen more clearly when it is moving. In the circumstances of a collision course, the relative bearing will remain constant, so peripheral vision will not be of much assistance if the possibility of a mid-air collision arises. Pilots can therefore adjust scanning techniques accordingly.

Night myopia

Some individuals who have perfect day vision may be myopic at night. It can cause problems because the pilot may be unaware, having such good day vision. Its origin lies in the differing colour frequencies at night and how the eye's lens focuses on them. In overall bad light the lens has enough focal capacity to see close objects (near-sightedness), but has problems for longer distances. Age, physical condition and other such factors also affect sight. Mild hypoxia through lack of oxygen degrades vision. It will appear as a reduction in light, which is important during night operations.

Visual clearing technique during flight

- Identifying any possible collision threat increases with time spent looking outside. Shifting the eyes and refocusing at frequent intervals is the best way.
- Visual scan should be in all directions and take in the entire sky area. The best results come from short, regularly spaced eye movements that progressively cover the sky. Develop your own scanning pattern, that way it will be more comfortable.
- Using peripheral vision is better to spot conflicting collision threats. This is because each time a scan is stopped peripheral vision takes over the primary detection of movement. Remember that at night a visual scan relies almost entirely on peripheral vision.

- Move the body as well as the head within the constraints of shoulder harness and seat belt. The combined movement can cover a vast area of sky and overcome cockpit obstructions, perhaps revealing conflicting traffic.
- Gentle turns as appropriate during climbs and descents help scanning, especially above and below the aircraft.
- Visual scanning is equally necessary and important on the ground. Before entering a runway for take-off scan the approach areas for traffic, even though you have a clearance.

Visual illusions

The eye provides good orientation so long as adequate reference points are available. Impulses from the cones and rods of the eye travel along the optic nerve to the brain. There is one disadvantage when trying to interpret visual cues when flying, as they look totally different from viewing them on the ground. In the air a pilot lacks stable visual references. Balance, or equilibrium, is easy to maintain when the ground can be seen. In this circumstance the eyes support and verify proprioceptive sensations – messages that are sent to the brain from the minute nerve endings in the muscles and tendons – and vestibular information, which is also important in balance, derived from the inner ear. Problems occur when the weather deteriorates or darkness falls and the view of the ground is lost. Without a visual horizon a pilot could select another, potentially dangerous 'reference line'. It might happen to be a sloping cloud bank, for example, as a substitute for the surface of the earth.

Summary of main illusions

Atmospheric Rain on the aircraft windscreen can give the impression of greater height, and haze (restricted visibility) of being further from the runway than you actually are. In thick mist a 'pitch up' illusion can cause the pilot to sharply steepen the approach angle.

Landing errors As we have seen with atmospheric problems that cause illusions, various surface features can give a false height and distance from the threshold touchdown point. Anticipation and knowing about them can help a pilot, plus the use of VASI and PAPI which will provide more precise judgement during the approach and landing.

Runway and sloping terrain An up-slope gives the impression the aircraft is *higher* than it is; a down-slope makes the aircraft seem *lower* than it actually is.

Ground Lighting Lights along a road and from moving vehicles can be mistaken for 'airfield lights'. In an area of comparative darkness, bright runway and approach lights make it seem as if there is less distance to the runway threshold. This can lead to the pilot flying a lower than normal approach to try to compensate.

Effects of rain

- reduces forward visibility
- gives objects an overall blurred effect
- causes a diffusion of light, which makes objects seem further apart and less intense, therefore further away than they are
- light is refracted causing a prismatic effect: a rain-covered windscreen causes an apparent downward displacement of objects and this makes the runway seem lower during an approach and landing

What must never be forgotten is that visual illusions seem very real. Recognising this fact and preparing for it is the only way of overcoming these problems.

Chapter 19
Anatomy of the Ear

Construction

In general terms the ear consists of three main parts: the outer, middle and inner ear (refer to Fig. 15). The outer ear is made up of the ear flap and the ear canal; the middle ear contains the ear drum, the auditory ossicles, which are sound-conducting bones, and the Eustachian tube; and the inner ear, sometimes called the inner tube, has the cochlea, being the organ of hearing, and the balance mechanism.

In essence the ear flap collects and channels the sounds along the ear canal to the ear drum. Sounds, which are merely small fluctuations in air pressure, make the ear drum vibrate. For the drum to be 'sound sensitive', the air in the middle ear must be at the same pressure as it is in the outer ear. This pressure is equalised by the Eustachian tube which connects the ear with the back of the throat. Therefore, when climbing and descending, a 'popping' sensation is often felt. This is the result of uneven pressures being equalised between the outer and middle ear.

The ear also has another function. It contains the balance organ. This is situated within the inner ear and consists of three inter-connected semi-circu-

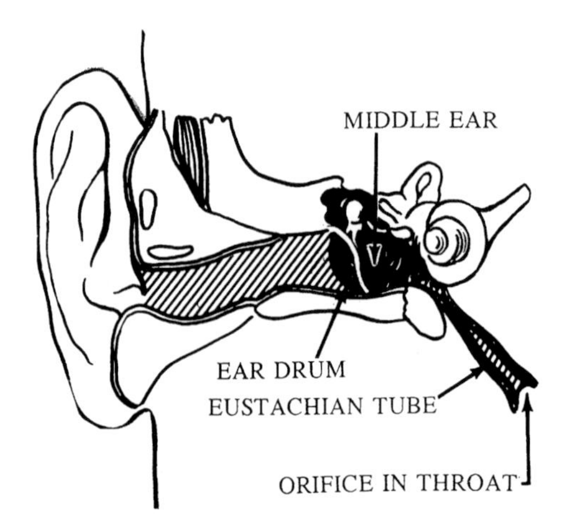

Figure 15 Ear structure and eustachian tube

How the Inner Ear Senses Movements and Attitudes

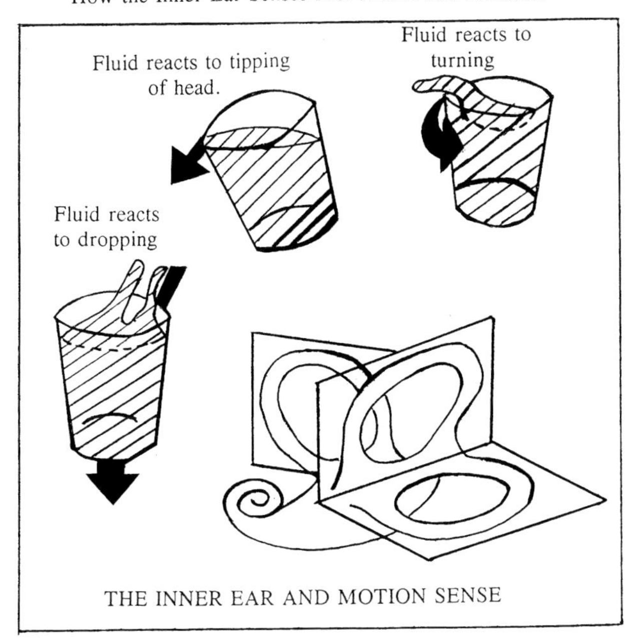

Figure 16

lar canals which contain fluid. As the head moves, the relative movement between the fluid and the canal displaces the receptor, which then sends a signal to the brain via the auditory nerve.

Sensations of the inner ear

A motion-sensing system is formed by the semi-circular canals. These are arranged at roughly right angles to each other, being in the pitch, roll and yaw axis. The system is shaped as in Fig. 16, and contains fluid and the sensory organs for detecting angular acceleration, as well as linear acceleration and gravity. Angular acceleration is detected through small sensory hairs that stick out into a gelatinous substance held in each canal. When the head starts to turn (causing angular acceleration), or when speeding up, slowing down and stopping, the sensory hairs in the axis of the turn in the canal are temporarily displaced. This is caused by the motion of the fluid lagging behind the motion of the canal wall. Impulses are then transmitted to the brain and a turning sensation is felt.

A gravity sensory organ for linear acceleration is situated in the bottom and side of a common sac. This also has small sensory hairs which project upward into more gelatinous substance containing chalk-like crystals. The weight carried by these sensitive hairs changes with every head movement, in whatever direction. This results in a sensation of tilting the head or body.

On the ground, man has adapted to sensory messages, but in the air this is a different story. Misleading messages can lead to disorientation, which can sometimes be serious according to how it affects the individual. We'll be considering equilibrium and sensory perception later.

Altitude change and its effects

Following Boyle's Law, the air in the middle ear cavity expands and contracts with changes in atmospheric pressure. If the pressure in the ear is not quickly equalised with the outside pressure during an altitude change, the ear drum can become inflamed and distended. Pain and temporary deafness can occur. This condition is called aerotitis.

The most discomfort can occur while descending. As the surrounding air pressure increases, the middle ear has already acclimatised to the reduced pressure at altitude, but is at a lower pressure than the external ear canal. As altitude decreases, the gradually increasing outside air pressure forces the ear drum to bulge inward. The condition is more difficult to relieve, but can be accomplished by frequent swallowing or yawning which contracts the small throat muscles, briefly opening the Eustachian tube. Pinching the nostrils and blowing gently can also bring relief. What is important is to make sure you ventilate the ears frequently during the descent. Reducing the aircraft's rate of descent also helps.

Aerosinusitis

Like aerotitis, this results from unrelieved expansion or contraction of air in the head sinuses. The sinus cavities surrounded by bones in the face and skull are grouped around the nasal passages. Two of the many pairs of sinuses are shown in Fig. 17 opposite. Each of the sinuses is connected to the nasal cavity by a narrow opening in the bone structure, lined with mucous membrane. You have no voluntary control over these openings as you have over the Eustachian tube, and any inflammation of the membrane prevents adjustment of pressure. Severe pain can result around the affected sinus.

Obstruction to pressure to adjustment is more likely to occur during a

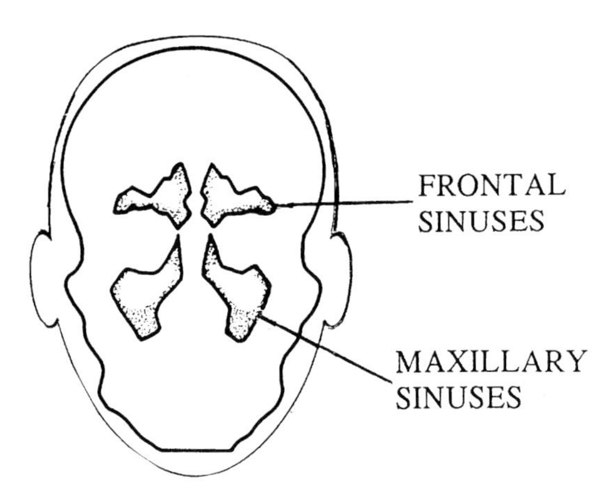

Figure 17 Sinuses

rapid descent. The only remedy if the condition is severe is to level off or climb until pressure equalises, then to descend at a reduced rate. The detrimental implications for the instrument pilot of these two conditions should be evident. If you have a severe cold, you are not likely to fly. However, with a minor cold, respiratory inflammation, or nasal allergy, you may think of flying after the usual dosage of medication. The possible effect of a head cold on your control of the aircraft under instrument flight conditions should be clearly understood. The effects of the drugs a pilot is most likely to encounter are as listed below.

DRUG	POSSIBLE EFFECTS
Antihistamines	Drowsiness, dizziness, nausea, headache, especially hazardous because the pilot may be unaware of drowsiness after initial alertness. Vision, coordination and equilibrium can also be affected.
Stimulants	Dilation of pupils and blurred vision, nervousness, impaired judgement.
Muscle relaxants	Sleepiness, weakness, vertigo.
Barbiturates	Initial excitement, then sleepiness and impaired mental and physical activity not appreciated by pilot.
Tranquillisers	Blurred vision, mental depression, sleepiness.

DRUG	POSSIBLE EFFECTS
Weight control agents (diet, pills, etc.)	Nervousness, errors in judgement, euphoria (feeling of well-being regardless of condition).
Anti-smoking agents	Nausea, discomfort and also distraction can result from the use of such drugs.

Sensory illusions

During VFR flight, orientation is maintained by the sense of sight in observing the attitude of the aircraft in relation to the earth's surface. While flying by reference to the natural horizon, therefore, the attitude of the aircraft can be readily detected at all times. During instrument flying when the natural horizon is no longer visible, the attitude of the aircraft in relation to the visual horizon we now know is obtained from the artificial horizon, or from a combination of other instruments.

The sense of sight is supported by other senses that help to maintain orientation. Sometimes during instrument flying these supporting senses conflict with what is seen. When this happens, there is a definite susceptibility to disorientation. The degree of disorientation may vary considerably with individual pilots, their proficiency and the conditions that induced it. Therefore it is important that you understand the senses by which orientation is maintained in order to successfully overcome the effects of false sensations.

Your ability to maintain equilibrium and orientation depends on signals from three primary sources: the motion-sensing organs of the inner ear, the postural senses which include touch, pressure and tension, and the sense of sight. If one of these sensory sources is lost, the ability to maintain equilibrium and orientation is considerably lessened.

Motion

The sense of motion which originates in the inner ear is very important to man in his normal environment – on the ground. The inner ear registers both linear and rotational acceleration and deceleration. It is able to detect most turns, slips and skids during flight. Unfortunately, it is not capable of distinguishing between centrifugal force and gravity, nor is it capable of detecting a constant velocity or small changes in velocity. False sensations from the inner ear also account for many illusions that are experienced during instrument flight referred to in the section on spatial disorientation. Centrifugal force and gravity are often coupled together in flight, and the resultant force cannot be interpreted without visual aid. For example, without visual aid, deceleration while turning can cause the inner ear to sense a reverse turn. Therefore the sensations from the inner ear during instrument flying are not reliable, and must therefore be disregarded.

Postural sense

The postural sense derives its sensations from the expansion and contraction of muscles and tendons, touch and pressure, and the shifting of abdominal muscles. These sensations are more readily experienced in flight than on the ground. Without visual aid, postural sense during flight often interprets centrifugal force as a sensation of rising or falling, which may be contrary to fact. Since the postural sense is not capable of detecting continued velocity without acceleration or deceleration, its sensations, like those of the inner ear, are unreliable in flight without visual aid. Without outside reference or flight instruments, you could interpret a steep bank to be a sharp climb, or a shallow descending turn to be straight-and-level flight. It is also important to realise that these false sensations sometimes occur when flying by instruments. Every pilot must learn to suppress these sensations when they conflict with what the flight instruments are showing.

Sight

When blindfolded you find standing somewhat more difficult than usual. To walk in a straight line while blindfolded is almost impossible, since normal reference to surrounding objects is lost. When standing on the ground, you are on a stationary platform from which the inner ear and postural senses may realise relatively reliable sensations. A somewhat different problem exists in flight, since you are on a moving platform. Without the aid of sight, your other senses are unable to distinguish between the sensations produced by gravity and those produced by centrifugal force. Your inner ear, which provides the sense of motion, is unable to detect small forces of acceleration and deceleration without aid from the sense of sight.

Visual illusions may sometimes occur as the result of attempting to fly by outside reference, when actual flight conditions demand reference to the flight instruments. Here are some examples of illusions:

- flight in and out of clouds can give the impression of rapid changes in speed and attitude
- reflected light on the canopy may give a false impression of a steep bank or even inverted flight

- lights on the horizon at night may appear to be at a much higher elevation
- the anti-collision light can produce a false impression of the aircraft in a turn when flying through clouds at night

Spatial disorientation

This can occur when the sensory organs send conflicting messages to the brain, which then leads to a state of confusion. Spatial disorientation is a false perception of the orientation of the aircraft. This is in respect to spatial references such as flight path and height.

Interactive forces which are complex and cannot be distinguished from the force of gravity can create special illusions unless directly corrected by sight. When outside visual reference is either restricted or obscured (either poor visibility or flying in cloud) correcting sensory information can only be satisfactorily accomplished by an instrument-trained pilot. The pilot must firmly believe what the instruments show.

Quite marked sensory illusions can occur even in level flight, also while turning, and the illusion of tumbling backwards if there is an abrupt change from climbing to level flight. In a banked turn while experiencing a positive g-force, then recovering to level flight, may cause the pilot to apply back pressure on the yoke, thinking the aircraft is diving. A significant reduction in airspeed results, and this shows the pilot the aircraft is not diving, so appropriate recovery action can be taken.

Disorientation during rotation (aerobatics)

Both disorientation and vertigo can occur if the aircraft is rolling, and the pilot moves the head out of the rotating plane. The effect can be severe. What happens is that two sets of semi-circular canals are stimulated. The same thing will happen after a harsh pull-out from a dive directly following a spin. Normally when a spin stops, there will be a sense of rotating in the opposite direction. This is due to the continuing rotation of the fluid. If there are poor visual cues, it is entirely possible for the pilot to put the aircraft into a spin in the opposite direction while correcting for this false illusion.

CHAPTER 20
HEALTH AND THE PILOT

How to keep yourself fit for flying

Physical fitness has been defined as the ability to meet a day's stresses without undue fatigue, to maintain reserve energy for recreational activities, and to rise to the challenge of unexpected demands. This is simply fitness for living. If a pilot is unfit, the physical discomfort of flying for four or five hours without a break can be exhausting. If the pilot also has poor muscle tone due to an inactive lifestyle, it is likely that the posture will be adversely affected, causing further discomfort. Then, if the flight has been turbulent, the stresses of countering it will cause fatigue more quickly in someone who is not physically fit. The overall effect of this increasing physical fatigue is a lowering of the ability to concentrate properly – very undesirable for a pilot.

Of course fitness alone is not sufficient protection against what we term 'aeromedical problems'. The pilot must also protect against other possible in-flight problems such as hypoxia and its opposite, an excess of oxygen causing hyperventilation. Then there are low temperatures, decompression sickness, which is similar to the bends following scuba diving, the strong possibility of food poisoning, and general fatigue through long duty hours at unsociable times (day and night operations). There is also carbon monoxide poisoning to watch out for. Stress, stressors and their effects have been covered in detail elsewhere in this book. In contrast, people who exercise regularly are often able to concentrate for longer periods of time, and to recover more quickly from fatigue.

Unfortunately, the calorific cost of piloting an aircraft, for instance, is only about half that of a train driver. If you combine this relative inactivity with poor eating habits and alcohol, the body weight starts to increase considerably. Remember the things you can do to increase your vitality and improve your flying performance. If you eat regularly and sensibly and work at reducing stress then you are well on the way to winning the fitness battle. Even a light exercise programme will improve your ability to concentrate, reduce fatigue and stress, and improve oxygen assimilation. This is particularly important for pilots. If you exercise moderately for up to forty minutes, three times a week, you will begin to experience some of the benefits. One way to help your exercise programme be successful is to make it as enjoyable as possible, not regard it as a chore merely to be endured. If you like to work out alone, then exercises such as jogging, walking and swimming may well suit you best; otherwise ball games or team activities might be better. Remember, if you are trying to lose weight, it took a while to put it on, and so it's going to take time to get it off. Be patient.

Pilot fatigue

A pilot suffers as much from the effects of fatigue as other people in society. There are three types of fatigue: muscular, mental and psychological.

One of the prime causes of pilot fatigue is responsibility. The very nature of the job is stressful. The mental load of course varies according to a number of factors; these include the number of take-offs and landings, route pattern, traffic density, weather encountered, aircraft type, technical and technological reliability and fellow crew members. The physiological factors that tend to produce and increase fatigue include hypoxia, or lowering of partial oxygen pressure of the lungs over long periods in a pressurised cabin, noise, vibration, excessively bright light, disturbance of eating and sleeping habits and wide variations of temperature and humidity. Physical factors which affect fatigue include age, for ageing brings with it lack of resilience and a lowering of physical fitness. Sleep deprivation and time zone changes also induce stress. Additional factors that cause fatigue are fear plus domestic and personal problems. All this simply emphasises the importance of a pilot being physically fit. If he is not, he will not be able to cope with fatigue.

Fatigue can be defined as a debt, both psychological and physiological. It arises from prolonged or intense physical or mental effort followed by inadequate rest. Fatigue is both individual and subjective. Crew rest compliance does not necessarily prevent it, nor a violation cause it. It can be said that fatigue may be acute or chronic. Acute fatigue can develop from any significant shortening in an individual's sleep cycle, from physical work, stress or simply long hours. Acute fatigue commonly accompanies circadian rhythm upsets, especially when travelling eastward (losing time). Crossing time zones to the east results in earlier bedtimes, when it's harder to fall asleep, and earlier wake-up times. For aircrew this type of 'sleep disruption' can cause additional stress as well as prolonged fatigue.

All humans have a daily (twenty-four-hour) activity/alertness/performance cycle roughly paralleling their temperature cycle. This reaches the 'low point' between one to two hours before the normal wake-up time. At these low points, people are generally most difficult to arouse and require more time to get going. The ability to adjust to time zone changes is improved by such factors as youth, good physical condition, mental motivation, out-going personality and stimulating social interaction.

Chronic fatigue can arise from work practices or sleeping difficulties. The worst hit seem to be at the management supervisory level, in other words the individual with a whole range of different job responsibilities. Check and training pilots are prime candidates for this. It can also be made worse by emotional strains, as well as financial or marital problems.

Fatigue is one of the major aircrew problems because it erodes judgement, compromises performance and predisposes one to illusions and disorders of attention. There is a loss of vigilance and alertness (degrading of vital situational awareness), a slowing of mental functions, and inattention. There can also be an acceptance of lower standards in performance (proficiency), forgetting items and making errors which go unnoticed.

Effects of fatigue in aircraft accidents

It has been established for many years that the mental and physical condition of a pilot is a contributing factor in many accidents. The effects of sleep loss or fatigue can be made worse by smoking, dehydration, caffeine and poor diet.

A classic example of how fatigue played a significant part in a fatal aircraft accident is the crash of a Mitsubishi MU-2 (N873Q) on 1 November 1979, near Nashville in the United States. The crash occurred at 2141 hours local time when the MU-2 went into a lake adjacent to Nashville Airport while on an approach to runway 31. The weather actual was clear sky with three miles visibility in ground fog. According to the NTSB report, the pilot reported the runway in sight at eight miles. At two miles the pilot confirmed his landing clearance. The tower controllers observed two bright flashes about a mile from the runway 31 threshold. The aircraft had passed through three high-tension lines approximately one and a quarter miles short of runway 31.

The MU-2 struck the power lines at 648 feet AMSL. The decision height (DH) for the ILS approach to runway 31 is 775 feet AMSL. The aircraft crashed into a lake two hundred yards past the power lines.

The NTSB investigation indicated that both engines and all instruments and electronics were operating normally at the time of the accident. The Safety Board blamed the pilot and the co-pilot for the crash. Significantly, they noted that the two pilots were *routinely* 'scheduled for eighteen–twenty hour crew duty times'. Sifting through all the mass of associated information, with particular reference to knowledge concerning the effects of sleep loss and fatigue, the full report is full of vital data providing an insight as to why the MU-2 crew made the errors they did.

The crew's schedule on the day they died started with an 0520 hours departure from Fayetteville, then to Houston. With only a short break it continued throughout the day until the accident at 2141 hours. In all accidents there are usually one or more contributing factors that set the scene for a mishap. In the case of the MU-2, there is no doubt that 'pilot fatigue' was a strong and major contributing factor. The fact that this particular crew had been routinely rostered on eighteen- to twenty-hour duty periods must support the deduction that a cumulative and perhaps chronic fatigue problem had built up in both pilots. The potential for committing serious errors of judgement increases in direct proportion to the amount and effects of fatigue.

As aircrew we have to be aware of what debilitating effects fatigue can have on us, mentally as well as physically. Medical evidence shows that fatigue caused by sleep loss is not related to the number of hours available to sleep, but *when* during the twenty-four-hour cycle those hours were available.

A report on the Diagnostic Classification of Sleep and Arousal Disorders lists the consequences of sleep loss and deprivation as fatigue, temperature, endocrine and metabolic inertia, sleepiness, lassitude, reduced vigilance, difficulty in concentration, uncoordinated movements, irritability, complacency, distractability and reduced motivation. A further NTSB report reveals some startling evidence from another fatal accident. As one veteran safety investigator put it, 'the two pilots involved were so under-performing [in terms of proficiency and loss of situational awareness] they were in themselves an accident looking for somewhere to have it'.

A Gates Learjet 25 had departed from Chicago at 0251 hours on its nightly schedule to Newark, New Jersey and Hartford, Connecticut with its cargo of cancelled bank cheques. The trip had been entirely uneventful. The Learjet had left FL410 and started its descent into the still darkened skies around the destination. Dawn was still a few minutes away, but from the advantage of height the two-pilot crew could already see the faint glow of dawn. That time of day has a special sort of tranquillity. The captain was a twenty-six-year old pilot with over 5,000 hours total flight time, including 1,600 hours on Learjets. He had flown the exact same route the previous night (except one investigator noted that the crew had forgotten to unload a bag of cheques at Newark). Special arrangements had been made by the captain to onward ship it to destination by regular airline. He had paid for it with a personal credit card in an attempt to conceal the mistake from his own company supervisor.

In the highly competitive world of night freight, including the lucrative business of flying cancelled cheques for the major banks, the consequences of mistakes leading to non-delivery can easily mean a contract being cancelled. (Most courier contracts are renegotiated every sixty to ninety days anyway, and considerable emphasis is placed upon on-time delivery.)

The co-pilot was only a year younger than his captain. At twenty-five he was also a well-qualified veteran of night courier services. In the previous ninety days he had logged 318 hours in the Learjet on night flights. There were other competing company Learjets following an identical route, and they had managed to beat one into Newark, gaining a few minutes. They made a fast turnaround and a fast flight to Hartford, where they off-loaded more packages of cancelled cheques. Here there was time for a quick breakfast at a nearby motel – or, as his co-pilot put it, perhaps it was dinner, so out of synchronisation was their natural twenty-four-hour body rhythm. Then it was time for crew rest before a 2300 hour departure westbound.

Background investigations revealed that both pilots led fast-paced lives. Both had left jobs with another courier service to be part of a newly-formed operation. In reality they had been dismissed from their jobs when a company vice-president had learned they were negotiating with the rival outfit. But like all new operations they had start-up problems. Colleagues close to the captain had noticed his interest in the new operation and his ambition to be successful. He was enthusiastic about the new company, the possibility of promotion and more responsibility. On the strength of his new job and better salary, the captain and his wife had bought a house, and she was expecting the couple's first child. Unfortunately, the new job clashed with external stresses: moving, the realities of being an expectant parent, the pressures of rapid change, and starting smoking again two years after kicking the habit. He had previously been a heavy smoker, and this included marijuana. The co-pilot shared an apartment with two other bachelors and had the typical lifestyle of a single person: late nights leading to irregular sleep patterns (which he already had anyway), fast foods and alcohol.

They began their descent into Newark, not really bothering with precision flying, but obviously urged into landing as fast as possible and getting the flight over with. Because of this lax attitude, they let the Learjet remain well over the 250 knot limit for speed below 10,000 feet. They requested a straight-in approach to runway 11 at Newark even though the wind was 340/09 knots. ATC denied the request due to night noise restrictions. The pilots also failed to fully compensate for a right-wing heavy fuel imbalance. During the approach they were in the process of cross-feeding fuel while trimming out the control forces.

With the airspeed indicating close to 180 knots and a ROD at 1,200 f.p.m., the Learjet turned on to a one-mile final for runway 04R where it slowed to 140 knots. This is five to ten knots fast even for a wing imbalance approach. They then descended at about 1,000 f.p.m. as they completed their approach at an estimated descent angle of about five degrees. Only thirty-three seconds elapsed between line-up and touchdown. Witnesses watched the aircraft hit the ground hard 500 feet beyond the runway threshold. It then 'bounced pretty hard', touched down again and bounced a second time to a height estimated at thirty feet, after which it rolled sharply to the right and crashed almost inverted. There was a brief fireball almost immediately, in which both pilots died as a result of injuries sustained with the impact.

The NTSB could find no mechanical cause for the accident. The fact that a Boeing 737 had landed four minutes before the Learjet's touchdown was ruled out as having any significance (wake turbulence, wing-tip vortices and the like). Nor did the Safety Board relate this accident to other incidents involving attempted go-arounds from very low speed, close to stall conditions. It is known that this Learjet was over-speed for the landing, and no evidence in the investigation suggests that the captain, who was manually flying the aircraft, initiated any go-around procedure. However, there is firm evidence that the crew, particularly the captain, was suffering from noticeable fatigue and definitely under-performing due to external pressures. For example, the captain had not fastened his seat belt for the landing. That failure might well have rendered him unable satisfactorily to operate the controls had he been dislodged from his seat after the initial hard bounce. An experienced crew does not deliberately fly an aircraft into an unstabilised approach, and then fail to anticipate the consequences of such an unsafe action. That is, unless they were preoccupied or badly distracted in some way.

Post-mortem toxicological examinations of each pilot's remains gave some indication of the stress their bodies and minds were under. In fact, qualitative tests showed that the captain had used marijuana within the previous twenty-four to forty-eight hours. (The medical report did make it clear that there was no proof he had smoked it within the immediate four to eight hours prior to his death.) The co-pilot had also been exposed to marijuana within the previous two days. It was not certain whether he had used it, or the positive traces found were from people around him who had used it (passive smoking). What was of greater significance was the level of carbon monoxide found in the two pilots' blood: three per cent in the captain, five per cent in the co-pilot.

The primary cause was smoking in combination with exposure to altitude. The NTSB stated that those two factors by themselves gave the crew an effective physiological altitude of 12,000 feet. This is sufficient to impair memory, attention and decision-making ability. Regardless of what they had been smoking, or when, that act of smoking was merely a manifestation of the pressure (stress) each pilot was experiencing. It is worth noting that the captain in particular had returned to smoking in response to the pressures of his newly acquired or perceived responsibilities. Probably neither pilot was aware of just how much he was demanding of his mind and body. In addition to the presence of chemical substances in their remains (in the case of the co-pilot it included a legal drug found in allergy medicine and diet pills), the time of the accident corresponded to a 'low period' in the human circadian rhythm, or biological clock. This was according to the Safety Board. As one investigator commented, 'For persons who keep the hours of a night courier pilot, who can say what would be a normal rhythm?' Their aircraft may have been serviceable enough, but their personal condition was definitely suspect on several counts.

It is normal practice to perform extensive and regular maintenance checks on aircraft engines and airframes for signs of wear and tear. So every aircrew member should be alert to stresses and cracks to the mind as well as the body. To do anything less ignores the most important element of preventive maintenance. You might well hold a first-class medical certificate, but are you really fit to fly?

Summary

- fatigue is a part of operational aviation and is something every aircrew member will experience
- the effects of fatigue can be insidious and can have long-term effects on the human body
- the flight environment itself is fatiguing brought on by vibration and noise; this can cause visual and motor problems
- illness can increase susceptibility to fatigue; pain and discomfort reduce the body's ability to withstand stress, both physical and emotional
- operational fatigue is an accumulation of effects from intense operations, demanding flight schedules involving long duty hours, and irregular rest periods and inadequate or incorrect diet; this upsets the biological clock, lowers mental alertness and degrades performance
- attitude and personal motivation can do a lot to combat fatigue; compounding factors can be reduced by including rest time to account for unusual flight times or time zone changes, eating balanced meals and allowing adequate fluid intake

Physiological changes seen with fatigue

- body temperature
- strength
- blood sugar (glucose)
- pupil response time to light (time for natural eye reflex to light)
- binocular fusion
- time for visual accommodation
- circulating blood volume
- heart rate
- eye fatigue
- muscle glycogen (energy stores)
- muscle co-ordination and control

Psychomotor changes seen with fatigue

- reaction time
- memory
- communication skill
- decision-making (slower)
- tracing (following object with eyes)
- irritability, anxiety, depression
- attention span
- errors
- co-operativeness
- acceptance of criticism
- activity
- personal care

CHAPTER 21

A TRAVELLING EXERCISE PLAN FOR AIRCREW

With pilots continually travelling and staying away from their home base, mostly in hotels, exercising effectively can become a problem. Therefore a series of mild but effective exercises are outlined below that can easily be accomplished in a hotel room.

Jogging on the spot: Start at an easy pace, lifting the feet four inches off the floor. Move about the room and keep up the pace for about three minutes.
Bent knee sit-ups: Bend your knees up so your feet are flat on the floor. With hands behind the head, sit up until your elbows touch the knees, then very slowly lower to the floor again. Repeat ten to fifteen times. You might need to lock your feet under the bed.
Sitting stretch: Sit on the floor with legs straight. Without bouncing, reach for both feet with both hands as far as you can and hold for a few seconds. You should feel it pull in the back of the legs. Do it ten times. It is more important to keep the legs straight than to reach the feet.
Push-ups: Lie on the floor on your stomach. Place your hands just out from your shoulders. Keeping the body straight, push up from the floor until the arms are straight. Lower slowly to the floor and repeat as many times as you can. (If you cannot keep your body straight, do push-ups from the knee.)
Shoulder shrugs: Stand erect, hands at sides. Slowly rotate your shoulders at your own speed, lifting up, back down and forward. Do ten forward and ten in the reverse direction.

In any event, check out the fitness facilities in the hotel where you are staying. If the hotel has a swimming pool (however small) use it.

Visual training in flight

There are some meaningful relaxation exercises that can be done in flight. They take very little time to accomplish, and you never need leave your cockpit seat. The exercises combine minimum effort and time with maximum efficiency.

Rotations: With your head looking straight ahead, move your eyes to the maximum limits, left to right, right to left, up and down, then in a large circle.
Fixations: Look at the aircraft nose, windscreen, infinity and back. This has the effect of loosening up the accommodative muscles.
Alternate eye blinking: Twenty times.
Full blinking: Twenty times.
Brock string: Using a piece of string with five knots in it, converge and diverge by looking at the knots. (One end of the string is held against the nose.)
Orthofusor training: This is the utilisation of a polaroid lens system and prisms. They are prescribed by a professional optician on an individual basis.

To obtain the best results, these series of visual exercises should be done at least one hour before landing at the destination airport.

CHAPTER 22

RECREATIONAL DRUGS VERSUS FLIGHT SAFETY

It has been known for years how recreational drugs such as alcohol, tobacco, caffeine and marijuana can dramatically affect aircrew performance, as we have seen in our examination of the fatal Learjet accident earlier. The USA NTSB and the accident reports of other countries are littered with references to the mental and physical effects of these drugs as contributory factors in aircraft accidents and incidents.

Aviation medical experts are increasingly concerned about this issue. You might argue that an occasional drink and smoke, perhaps ten or twenty a day, couldn't have any real effect on your performance. You are wrong; it could. Cigarettes, coffee, tea and alcohol can have a subtle and often serious impact on flight safety. If we include the effects of the illicit recreational drug, marijuana, it can be worse. One researcher found a startling increase in marijuana usage among aircrew. It was almost as acceptable as smoking cigarettes. Regulatory bodies and aviation operating companies have pretty strict guidelines for aircrew regarding alcohol or other substances, and indeed for other personnel in safety-critical areas. General regulatory wording usually takes this form: A person acting as a member of the operating crew of an aircraft for the purpose of so acting shall not, while so acting or carried, be in a state which, by reason of his or her having consumed, used, or absorbed any alcoholic liquor, drug, pharmaceutical or medicinal preparation or other substance, renders his or her capacity so to act impaired.

Alcohol

In the United States, about seven per cent of aviation accidents are related to alcohol misuse. Simulator studies around the world have time and again demonstrated that as blood alcohol concentrations increase, serious error rates rise. Failures of vigilance and lapses in crew co-ordination also increase. These problems were found even at the lowest alcohol level studied, 0.025 per cent. A daily ethanol intake of 80gm or more exposes a person to possible disease, including damage of the liver, central nervous system, gastro-intestinal tract and heart. An intake of 100gm per day or more is hazardous. (A normal beer contains about 6gm per 100ml; table wines contain 8–11gm per 100ml; spirits 32–40gm per 100ml.

Habitual use of alcohol results in:

- central nervous system tolerance, in which the dependent person can sustain an increasing alcohol intake yet go about his or her business at a blood alcohol concentration that would incapacitate the non-tolerant drinker
- peripheral nervous system disease which can produce altered sensation and function of the lower limbs due to irreversible nerve damage
- organ damage resulting from toxic effects on cells, particularly in the liver, central nervous system, gastro-intestinal tract and heart
- interference with vision, balance, co-ordination and motor functions
- predisposition to other serious diseases such as diabetes, pancreatitis, epilepsy and vitamin deficiency syndromes
- serious impairment of psychomotor skills, reaction times, judgement, decision-making and cognitive function

Alcohol abuse is a potent contributory factor in aircraft accidents, the same way it is factored into motor vehicle and industrial accidents. In Australia, alcohol-related disease is a significant cause of temporary or permanent loss of aviation qualifications. For up to seventy-two hours after even mild intoxication, there can be measurable degradation of psychomotor performance, decision-making, visual acuity and the ability to track and maintain a target; a zero blood alcohol level, even in the presence of hangover symptoms, does not equate to the return of normal human performance.

If you have a hangover it can affect any safety-critical procedure. Changes to the density of fluid in your ear canals due to alcohol can affect your balance, and are compounded by hypoxia and turbulence. Your fine motor skills will be impaired, and you will find yourself flying less smoothly and have more susceptibility to disorientation and motion sickness. If you try to offset fatigue with an increase of caffeine and cigarettes, you will further interfere with your metabolic, physiological and cognitive functions.

Caffeine

How many times have we asked a cabin attendant for yet another cup of coffee on a long night flight? Too many, perhaps, because we feel in need of a 'pick-me-up'.

After drinking coffee (average caffeine content between 75 and 100 milligrams), the caffeine is almost completely absorbed within fifteen to forty-five minutes, the clinical effects lasting approximately three hours. Research evidence suggests that complex decision-making and problem-solving are unaffected by caffeine consumption. However, some harmful effects are recognised: caffeine is a diuretic and can cause dehydration; and suddenly stopping a regular caffeine intake can be associated with some unpleasant withdrawal effects such as irritability, difficulty in concentrating, headache, tremor and difficulty in sleeping.

Tobacco

There is no question that the dangers of tobacco smoking are well documented and backed up by overwhelming medical evidence. It can cause serious cardiovascular disease, bronchitis, emphysema and lung cancer. Smoking impairs the haemoglobin transport of oxygen in the blood to vital organs, reducing its effectiveness by up to ten per cent. It can also have subtle, usually unnoticed cerebral effects, especially if compounded by altitude-induced hypoxia and cold.

Above 4,000 feet the effects of smoking become apparent, in particular the impairment of night vision and visual acuity. Colour perception is also reduced. Although withdrawal effects after stopping smoking vary considerably, it can result in nausea, headaches, increased appetite, irritability and insomnia. Symptoms may persist for weeks and sometimes longer.

Research has shown that three cigarettes smoked at sea level can raise your physiological altitude to 8,000 feet. The reason goes back to the characteristics of haemoglobin. This combines with oxygen in direct proportion to the oxygen partial pressure in the lung cells. Tobacco smoke also exerts a partial pressure along with the other gases inhaled. It is the minute amount of carbon dioxide in tobacco smoke that can seriously affect your physiological altitude, for two reasons. First, haemoglobin combines with carbon monoxide approximately two hundred times as readily as it does with oxygen. Once this is combined, the resistance to separation is in the same proportion. Secondly, regardless of oxygen partial pressure, combination of haemoglobin with carbon monoxide reduces the amount of haemoglobin available to carry oxygen and carbon dioxide. Thus, the longer the carbon monoxide is available in the lungs, even in minute amounts, the less oxygen is carried in the blood.

Marijuana

The immediate effects of smoking marijuana include the creation of a pleasant, dreamlike state, with impairment of attention, cognitive and psychomotor performance. This appears reversible to the person smoking it. Because of its perceived lack of acute, life-threatening effects, cannabis has been termed a soft or recreational drug. It has been described as no more damaging than coffee or tobacco. Medically this is not true, as the drug's impairing effects are on memory and learning, as well as on the lungs, immune defences, brain and reproductive function.

Many polyaromatic hydrocarbons have been identified in marijuana smoke, some of which are known to be carcinogenic. There is also strong evidence to suggest that (like tobacco smoking) it can cause cancer of the mouth, larynx, tongue, upper jaw and respiratory tract. Cannabis and its by-products are highly fat soluble and are stored in the body's fat, liver, lung and spleen for lengthy periods. Its longer-term effects, although not known in any detail, are certainly adverse to human health.

The aftermath (day after) effects of marijuana can lead to mood swings, lack of alertness and impairment of the operation of complicated equipment. Some reports suggest that marijuana may be up to 4,000 times more potent (that is gram for gram) than alcohol, in producing decrements in the performance of subjects studied under controlled conditions. Heavy usage runs the risk of experiencing psychotic symptoms. Over a long period, there could be subtle forms of cognitive impairment which persist while the user remains chronically intoxicated. The additional downside of this is that it may not reverse after abstinence.

There is definitely no place for any form of cannabis use in the aviation environment. Even the infrequent, so-called recreational user of cannabis could easily put others at risk the day after smoking it.

Summary

Alcohol For up to seventy-two hours after even mild intoxication, there is a measurable degradation of psychomotor performance, decision-making, visual acuity, and the ability to track and maintain a target. The effects are aggravated by altitude-induced hypoxia and reduced temperature.

Caffeine Can cause dehydration. Withdrawal effects can lead to difficulty in concentrating.

Tobacco Impairs oxygen-carrying ability of the blood. At 8,000–10,000 feet visual acuity and colour perception are reduced.

Marijuana Impaired attention, cognitive and psychomotor performance for at least twenty-four hours, possibly longer.

CHAPTER 23
INCAPACITATION DURING A FLIGHT

Incapacitation of a flight crew member during the course of a flight can be a very serious matter. In fact, certain pathological conditions have been a factor in varying degrees in some aviation accidents and incidents.

On a multi-crew flight deck the incapacitation of one member can usually be handled, but considerable difficulties can arise if there is only one pilot. If it is partial incapacitation it could easily be missed by other members of the crew. Even the affected individual may not be fully aware of what is happening. Any form of illness or general discomfort can lead to a degrading in mental performance and affect the pilot's decision and judgement-making ability. Here are some of the more common causes of incapacitation in flight:

- stress, fatigue, dieting, disturbance of circadian rhythm
- the side-effects of medication
- gastro-intestinal disorders (a common ailment for pilots in the tropics)
- heart attacks and other cardiovascular problems (there have been some disastrous accidents resulting from these)
- carbon monoxide in the cabin (insidious, and a real killer)
- bladder problems, urinary infection, kidney stone attacks
- lack of oxygen
- the effects, or after-effects, of the common cold leading to blocked sinuses which can cause real pain and discomfort, usually worse during the descent
- ear infections of varying degrees – changes in altitude (climbing or descending) can cause pain

It is basically up to the captain to determine if any crew member appears to be suffering from any of these physical problems before the flight, then take whatever action is necessary, even replacing the crew member with someone on standby. However, if incapacitation does take place, dealing with the problem can be somewhat more difficult, particularly if it is really serious and there is no immediate medical help. Breathing ailments, dizziness and sometimes nausea can be helped by using portable oxygen usually available on the flight deck or in the cabin. If there is no medical help and the individual appears to be in a serious condition, then the flight should be curtailed and a diversion made to the nearest suitable airfield. Of course air traffic control must be told at the earliest opportunity. This particularly applies in the case of passenger incapacitation. If a pilot-seat crew member is affected, then it is important to make sure that his or her safety harness (particularly shoulder restraints) are secure and tight so as to prevent the body collapsing across the controls.

The dangers of flying after scuba diving

Anyone contemplating flying after scuba diving should allow the body sufficient time to get back to normal, that is, to get rid of excess nitrogen absorbed during diving. If this is ignored there is a strong possibility of decompression sickness from dissolved gas. This can occur even at low altitudes. The in-flight problems can be very serious. Bear in mind that most pressurised commercial passenger aircraft maintain a cabin altitude of around 8,000 feet. As far as flying after scuba diving is concerned, the recommendation is that you do not fly for at least twelve hours to a height, or cabin pressure altitude, of 8,000 feet; more specifically twelve hours after diving which has not required controlled descent (such as diving straight off a beach or in a group from a boat), or at least twenty-four hours after diving from a controlled descent. The waiting time before any flight planned to exceed cabin pressure altitudes of 8,000 feet after any scuba diving should be at least twenty-four hours.

Summary

As a pilot you have considerable responsibilities. This applies not only to the operational flying aspects, but to other crew members and passengers. Before flying ask yourself:

- Am I fit to fly (physically and mentally)?
- Do my crew appear fit? If necessary, ask questions.
- Remind the cabin attendant(s), if carried, that they must report any passenger who appears to be in distress or discomfort, or is obviously ill *before the flight starts*.

CHAPTER 24

PILOT JUDGEMENT AND DECISION-MAKING

As aircrew we are continually making judgements about a whole range of aviation issues: how much fuel we need for a particular flight, the number of passengers we can carry, is the performance of the aircraft adequate for the route, and do we have suitable alternative airfields? Unfortunately, we read and hear about aircraft accidents that seem to happen all too frequently. Pilot error or bad judgement is talked about as the primary cause: 'Flying into adverse weather and getting off course, then crashing into high ground'; 'Running out of fuel'; 'The aircraft was overloaded and was unable to maintain altitude when an engine failed'. There is a long list of reasons we could think of.

Over half the accidents caused by pilots in civil flying relate to bad pilot judgement. From the point of view of the general public, it would be easy to deduce that there must be some truth in the opinion that a number of pilots definitely have very poor judgement. This might be true in one or two cases, but not in general. Nevertheless, aviation 'trainers' believe that judgement is a skill that can be learned. Because 'decision-making' involves the human element, it is subject to a range of problems. These include:

- mistakes in the operation of aircraft systems
- misreading instrument indications
- lack of in-depth knowledge and understanding of the specific aircraft type being flown, which leads to:
  - slow use of checklists, skipping and/or misreading items
  - lowering of situational awareness and fatigue
  - increase of stress factors, leading to cockpit task saturation which can cause serious human errors with vital information being ignored
  - fatigue, leading to an inability to function at an acceptable and safe level
  - a lack of confidence, especially for low-experience pilots, when encountering bad weather
  - a low standard of flight proficiency through lack of training leading to the development of bad habits
  - personal psychological problems (marital, financial, etc.) which create underlying distractions leading to task errors on the ground and in-flight.

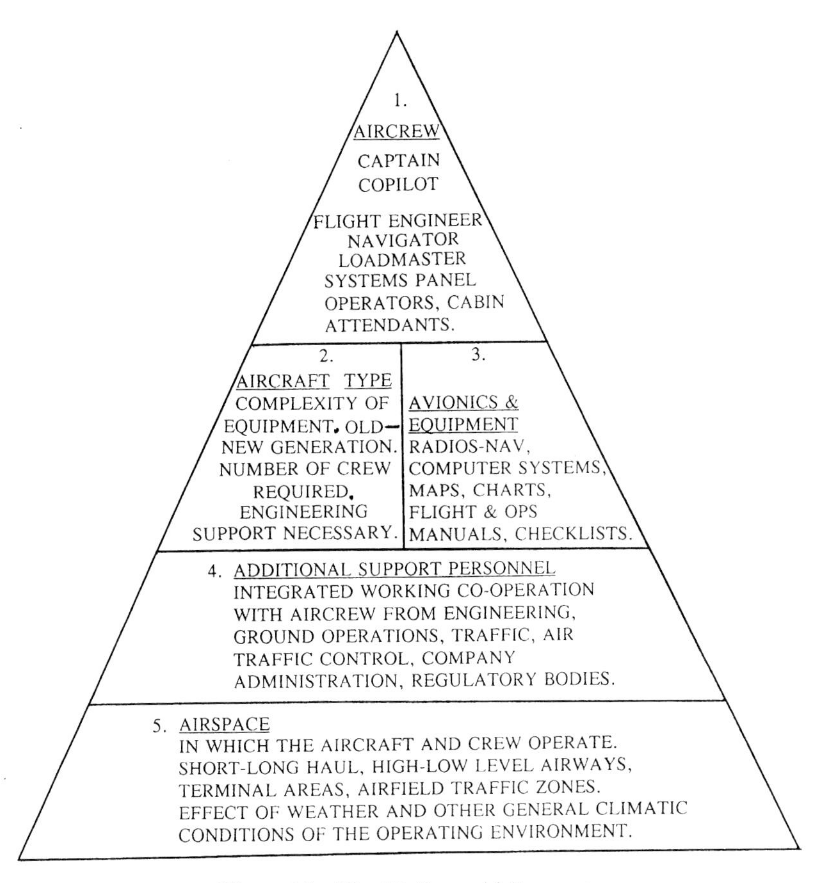

Figure 18 The 5A Pyramid Concept

Let's examine the 5A Pyramid Concept I've developed showing the areas in which judgements have to be made (Fig. 18). At the top of the pyramid is the flightcrew, the principal member being the pilot-in-command. (All aircrew play an important part in the operation of the aircraft and associated duties, with the captain being the final decision-maker.) The flightcrew as an integrated unit (or a pilot as an individual) have to 'manage and control' all the components of the pyramid in such a way that it results in a safe flight.

This is the vital human element and the most involved, because it makes the key cognitive and perceptual judgements and decisions. *Any* problems from whatever source that create distraction of any kind not only lower overall situational awareness, but degrade the mental processes. Cognitive judgement can be described as a mental process concerning a pilot's attitude to taking risks. This involves the individual's mental ability to evaluate these risks, and make a correct decision based on overall knowledge and experience. Perceptual judgement concerns decisions relating to sensations and perceptions which directly influence the pilot in physically controlling the aircraft; for example, visually judging terrain clearance in mountainous areas, distance, speed, etc.

It is evident from this analysis that cognitive and perceptual judgements are part of every action a pilot takes. In many cases they are both being used at the same time. If we look at an example, it is easy to understand. During an approach to land perceptual judgement helps the pilot control the aircraft on the correct glidepath – airspeed with elevators and power for rate of descent, right down to runway threshold. The cognitive judgement is exercised in the pilot's decision on when to 'flare out' in preparation for the landing. Similarly, if we fail to keep a good lookout when flying in a busy traffic pattern of an airport and cause disruption, this is poor cognitive judgement. So is a late turn on to final approach which overshoots the extended runway centreline.

The two judgements we have been discussing fall under the umbrella of situational awareness. We need a high degree of situational awareness at all times, which brings in the additional factors of lookout and time. There are many examples highlighting poor judgement. Here are a few:

- trying to accomplish too many tasks at the wrong time
- not completing essential checklist items in the right place at the right time
- ignoring something that should be done
- not exercising correct command authority by letting other (less experienced) crew members influence decisions you know to be right

The two forms of judgement can be described as the start and end of a continuous chain of elements, as portrayed below:

Perceptual Judgement
Visual Perceptions
- Distance
- Altitude
- Speed
- Obstacle clearance

Cognitive Judgement
Thought Processes
- Initially learning to fly
- Instructional flying is cognitive

As we progress and gain experience we *see* and *know* virtually automatically without intensive evaluation and thought. When this happens we are moving from cognitive back to perceptual. By doing this we can begin to make good judgements automatically. We can help ourselves in that process of judgement-making by following a number of related steps. By understanding each of these steps we can be made more aware of the process in developing better judgement.

- Vigilance as the first step to awareness. Looking for problems that might occur. Preparation and expectation.
- Discovering the problems that can alter the flight and the possibility of any one affecting safety. This requires good deductive capacity in addition to perceptual skills.
- Analysing problems. The pilot finds out what the problem is. This means the ability mentally to process all the factors, use existing knowledge in the brain's memory banks, and then use problem-solving skills.
- Deciding on alternatives. At this stage the pilot decides on what alternatives are available, and which ones to adopt to solve the problem. This not only requires a certain depth of knowledge but also creativity.
- Analysis of risk factors. The pilot determines the risks involved for each alternative course of action decided upon. This will involve using diagnostic mental computing skills, and this stage may very well take place as an extension of, or in conjunction with, deciding on alternatives.
- Background problems. It refers to the non-safety factors that affect every cognitive decision made by the pilot. This can include fatigue, economics, commercial and management pressures and commitment to the job. Handling these problems requires mental discipline and stamina.
- The formulated decision. A final decision has been made by the pilot, who is now ready to implement the plan. Within the multi-crew environment this means exercising leadership skills.
- Actioning the decision. This can involve things like physically flying the aircraft, climbing, descending, altering course, changing the flight plan; even passenger liaison and the provision of in-flight information. Therefore a whole range of 'judgement' skills can be brought into use: physical (professional), mental and inter-personal.

The whole process of judgement requires several abilities: observation; perception and information-processing skills; overall knowledge, and how to solve problems by using that knowledge; mental strength, creativity and discipline; and leadership and inter-personal social skills.

When I first started flying many years ago, judgement was based on pure experience. Therefore overall knowledge and a long period in which skills were developed became an integral part of being able to make the right judgements. These elements were put together under the heading of 'airmanship'. So if we have good airmanship, we are also exercising good judgement. We can also adapt our pyramid concept to define airmanship. If we break this down into various parts, we can better understand what is involved (Fig. 19). In pilot

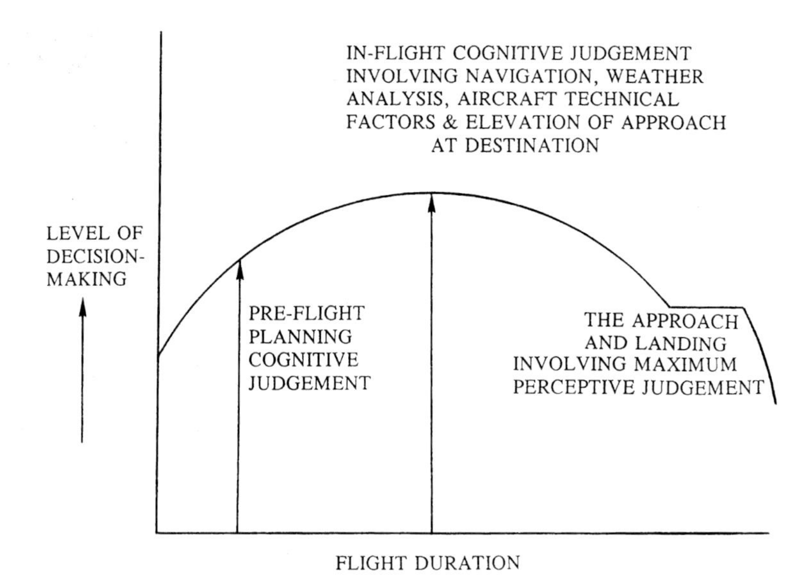

Figure 19 Levels of judgement and decision-making versus flight duration

training all these parts are incorporated in the 'building block' method, both before and during each training period.

If we expand the original 5A Pyramid Concept to include the additional risk factors involved in military operations, there are many additional variables to consider. Therefore, selecting, evaluating and training military aircrew needs a great deal of experience and expertise.

Knowledge, skill and experience

Pilot training in civil aviation is mainly concerned with the development of perceptual and motor skills, particularly in the early stages. Experience follows as a logical progression. Skill is the ability of an individual to successfully complete a task requiring special knowledge or ability. In aviation it is largely these 'physical' (motor) skills that attract most attention, in other words, the precision with which the pilot flies the aircraft by handling the controls.

However, there are other important and related skills a pilot must have to function effectively and safely in the 'aviation environment'. These relate to pre-flight planning, navigation (visual and electronic), plus a knowledge of basic aircraft engineering and maintenance procedures. The basic knowledge is of course learned through theoretical study and practical application in flight school; the degree of skill achieved after this comes mainly through experience from continual practice. The degree of expertise that is developed depends on the aptitude and learning ability of the individual.

It should be realised that all types of training create some degree of behavioural changes. This affects attitudes towards particular situations and problems. Therefore it is essential to perceive the situation, identify the problem, consider all alternatives to overcome it, and then arrive at a sensible judgement and take a decision. Judgements are likely to be based on one, or a combination, of the following categories of behaviour and ability.

- Knowledge, which depends on memory
- Understanding, relating to the measure of perception
- Regulations, determined by rules and procedures
- Perceptual skill, relating to the practical technique of doing something

Arriving at a final decision will consist of both mental and physical functions that may be affected by the amount of available time.

Cognitive judgement results from perceiving any particular situation through the senses or memory. The brain's 'memory banks' then have to analyse the situation, or problem, and decide how to deal with it. A pilot will be using knowledge acquired through previous experience. This will involve consideration of his/her own ability, and the technical capability of the aircraft to carry out the required action. This will also take into account whether any alternative plan is feasible (or preferable).

If we look at the development of a pilot's (perceptual) aircraft general handling skills, we might come across the term 'precognitive control'. It is certainly an accurate description of how a pilot achieves a higher performance level. Specifically this occurs when the pilot knows exactly what to do because he/she is totally familiar with the aircraft systems and handling characteristics. We know that through training and constant practice (actual training and everyday operational flying) a pilot becomes very proficient, in terms of precise control movements that are accurately timed and carried out. The aircraft can then be flown to tight practical limits. The by-product of this is accurate ILS (CAT II limits requiring special aircrew certification), VOR-DME, ADF, plus SIDs and STARS. Of course this needs good cognitive judgement skills as well.

Exercising judgement

We have seen in some detail how human beings have the unique capacity and ability to evaluate and store information from a great many sources, then with training and experience arrive at a considered (judgement) conclusion. The one problem with judgement is that it can be quite badly affected by psychological pressures, meaning:

- stress
- personality/behavioural problems (dominant, hyper, introverted)
- lack of appropriate knowledge
- inability to apply existing knowledge to the situation or problem

Basic judgement training concerns the pilot and other flightcrew, the aircraft, the environment, technical capabilities and parameters, and time constraints. All these factors have elements of risk which concern every flight. This could mean unexpected technical or weather problems. On the other hand psychological factors also play a part, such as the mental attitude of the crew trying to avoid a night-stop away from home due to a delayed departure. This could mean cutting safety margins.

To exercise good judgement, a potential or embryo hazard must be detected and all the factors considered. For the risk to be minimised, or eliminated, action must be taken then watched carefully to see that it is working properly. Good judgement and decision-making must be based on the very highest standards of experience and ability.

A two-part step towards good judgement

Once we have evaluated and understood judgement we can look one stage further and reduce the eight-step 'judgement model' into two parts. The first part is mental, relating to the brain's activities, the second, attitude.

Mental relates to the ability to find out and decide on the relevance of all available information directly concerning the flight, evaluation of the problems in an expeditious manner, and specifying alternative courses of action while assessing risks associated with each one.

Attitude is the motivation to select and carry out a viable course of action within available time constraints. Selecting what to do could mean taking some action (changing the profile of the flight), or simply monitoring what was happening; 'viable' means it will work within the normally accepted pattern of aviation judgement.

Pioneers of pilot judgement

Good judgement can be very elusive. It is even more difficult to accomplish when you are sitting on the ground. Nevertheless, the pioneers of flight, the Wright brothers, seemed to have the whole thing in complete perspective right

The Wright brothers, aviation pioneers in every sense, made their first powered flight in the Wright Flyer, on 17 December 1903. They were very safety conscious throughout all their experimental flight trials, only moving forward one step at a time, when they considered it safe to do so. Indeed, an early form of Flight Safety Management
(*Photo: Courtesy Flight International*)

from the very beginning – and at that time they hadn't even tried 'powered flight'.

In 1901, just two years before they succeeded, Wilbur Wright wrote in a letter to a friend (quoted in Coombs in 1979): 'All who are practically concerned with aerial navigation agreed that the safety of the operator (meaning the pilot) is more important to successful experimentation than any other point. The history of past investigation demonstrates that greater prudence is needed rather than greater skill. Only a madman would propose taking greater risks than the greater constructors of earlier times.' We can easily see from this that the success of the Wright brothers was due in great measure to extremely good judgement and intellect.

While other so-called aviation pioneers were being killed in risky flights jumping out of balloons and off high bridges, even cliffs, seeking to be lauded as the first to fly, the Wrights were taking their flying experiments slowly, step by careful step. They practised for several years away from the public eye and the attendant publicity it attracted. In fact they chose to try out all of their experimental 'flights' close to the ground across undulating sand dunes. Not for them the giant leap into the air in a 'do or die' effort, like some of their contemporaries. In all the Wrights made over 900 glider flights away from public crowds. By following this plan they said that they could give all their attention to the real task of building up experience towards their ultimate goal of powered flight. Indeed they made no attempt even to try to install an engine and fly until they were reasonably certain of their skill, and that the 'aircraft' was capable of flying. Certainly they wanted to avoid the highly publicised disasters of their contemporary 'inventors'.

Chapter 25
Casual Factors in Aircraft Accidents

If we look at published aircraft accident summaries, many miscellaneous so-called 'casual factors' are included. Some typical examples include:

- the pilot continued even though the weather was deteriorating rapidly
- the pilot lost control of the aircraft
- the pilot was flying beyond his level of experience
- an engine failure was misidentified by the crew, resulting in confusion, with subsequent excessive height loss leading to a collision with high ground below the Minimum Safety Altitude (MSA)
- the aircraft overshot the end of the runway following a high and fast approach in poor weather conditions

In the last example, it was no fault of the aircraft that it flew a high and fast approach, or the fact that it ran off the far end of the runway. This was all due to bad judgement by the pilot, which translates into pilot error when it is written into the accident report. The above, and the rest of the examples I have quoted, are extracts from actual accident reports.

When we consider 'operations at minimum level' (misleadingly referred to as 'low flying'), exercising good judgement through experience is an absolute prerequisite. Low-level flying by pilots inexperienced in this type of operation has led to many accidents.

Good and bad judgement

In flying, we all know it is simply not the case of 'pressing on regardless' whatever the problems. Unfortunately there are some pilots who do. I have come across one or two with this 'Rambo' complex, but they did not last long.

Just before an early morning flight one of these pilots asked for his aircraft to be fully fuelled (it was a high-wing machine with the refuelling points on top). The fueller left both filler caps loose so the pilot could easily check they were full. Unfortunately, in the poor light just after dawn (it was an airstrip beside a safari camp in the African bush), the pilot neglected to complete his pre-flight check and the filler caps remained loose. So *en route* to the destination he noticed the fuel gauges were going down very quickly. He thought (quite wrongly) that they were 'only Mickey Mouse gauges anyway, and never gave an accurate reading' (only partly true). He continued with the flight and reached his destination, stopping just long enough to off-load the passengers. Half-way back to his home airport the engine suddenly stopped while he was over high ground. (He had not completed any pre-flight inspection of the aircraft prior to take-off for the return flight.) The aircraft crashed in a rocky gully and the pilot was killed. Fortunately there were no return passengers.

The aircraft ran out of fuel because a considerable quantity 'vented' out of the tanks due to the loose filler caps (the low pressure over the wings syphoning fuel into the air down to a certain level). When the pilot saw the gauges going down so quickly, he should have returned to base immediately, knowing something was wrong.

The passengers carried on the outbound flight were later questioned by an air accident investigator. It turned out one of them had flown regularly as a passenger in the same type of light charter aircraft. He stated that he became worried about the fuel gauges (they were directly in front of him where he sat in the right-hand front co-pilot seat), and had pointed this out to the pilot. He said his worries had been brusquely dismissed, with the additional comments that it was a minor technical problem (only the pilot's perception) and he had to get the aircraft back to base anyway to avoid delaying a later charter flight. (Certainly symptomatic of the 'Rambo' press-on-regardless complex.) In the final analysis, the reason the pilot was killed was not because of a bad forced landing, but the fact he did not have his seat belt fastened. Investigators said there was every chance he would have survived the crash.

Hazardous attitudes to watch out for

- impulsiveness
- machismo ('Rambo' complex)
- anti-authority
- being too tentative
- invulnerability
- resignation
- weather bandits (trying to out-smart the weather)
- no effort to flight plan properly
- over-confidence (one of the main killers)
- bad mental discipline leading to a loss of essential situational awareness

Management pilots have a responsibility to ensure that the pilots working within their company's operation are 'fit' to do so. Some obvious hazardous attitudes in the above list are relatively easy to spot, others are not. I'm referring to the psychological traps a pilot can fall into. Let's take a brief look at these. (Strictly speaking each one we will mention could be termed behavioural. However, all have psychological reasons for existing.)

Weather bandits
Weather bandits are those pilots who take chances with weather, bust minimum descent altitudes during instrument approaches, and often in general aviation operations in light aircraft creep along under low cloud bases (reporting VFR) when they are really in instrument conditions. Pilots of this nature are impatient about weather delays in general, and are too lazy to file IFR because of the inconvenience of coping with yet another task. They also do not seem to be fully aware of the dangers involved as a result of what they are doing. It is a fact that there have been more fatalities in general aviation caused by weather-related accidents than any other single factor.

Uncertain or tentative pilot
One who is afraid or unwilling to carry through what should be done. For example, I checked out a type-experienced pilot on a Shorts 330, which is renowned as difficult to handle in a cross-wind. On landing this pilot almost lost control in only a moderate cross-wind simply because he was tentative about using full inter-wind aileron. After I had demonstrated this to a satisfactory conclusion, he tried again and was only marginally better. This was a captain with over 450 hours on type. The following day we had another training (proficiency) session, and although there was some improvement he still had some anxious moments controlling the aircraft in a cross-wind.

Bad flight planning preparation
This is not restricted to inexperienced student pilots who are in the 'learning process'. When pilots become more experienced, particularly when flying fully IFR-equipped aircraft, they often tend to put little or no effort into flight planning. They argue that it takes too much time and the prepared flight plan is superseded by airborne events anyway. 'We'll check the weather in the air and work it all out then.' How often have we heard that! The problems then start *when they're in the air*, probably encountering IFR conditions and being faced with a high cockpit workload. Because of this there is inevitably some loss of situational awareness and a degrading of proper vigilance (airmanship, lookout, maintaining communications and, of course, navigating the aircraft).

Loss of situational awareness
Personal discipline, awareness of what is going on around you, using all the facilities at your disposal (as a pilot) to the best operational advantage. Monitoring fuel consumption and obtaining weather updates, together with

liaison with the rest of the crew and ensuring the comfort of the passengers and all aspects of flight safety. Your situational awareness can degrade very quickly if you lose track of any of these essential elements. Any such situation can lead to mistakes being made, or a potential incident situation arising that puts pressure and stress on the pilot.

Over-confidence
A personal assumption a pilot makes that he knows (or believes) he knows everything that is necessary about flying. This leads to lack of flying discipline and being unprepared in dealing with a major problem should it arise. It increases the possibility of having an accident.

Some conclusions about judgement

Good judgement is not something you can easily pin down. On the ground good decisions are easy to make. The situation changes, though, when pressures suddenly start and a tight flight schedule has to be completed on time. Other considerations enter the 'operational picture' and new evaluations and decisions have to be made.

What is often perceived as a pilot's bad judgement does not always result in a bad outcome, which can influence, conflict with and hamper the development of good judgement for others. This would be especially true in the case of an inexperienced pilot, one who is working in a company where well-established older pilots often appear to ignore the elements of good aviation judgement in favour of appeasing company commercial pressure and/or maintenance problems. Our perception can also be distorted when a bad decision (judgement) is made and nothing happens. For the young, inexperienced pilot, it could have the effect of making a poor decision seem not so bad after all. If that pilot were faced with a similar operational situation, the same risk is more likely to be taken.

CHAPTER 26

THE HUMAN BRAIN – INFORMATION PROCESSOR

The brain is a unique powerhouse of information and it is an easy matter to underestimate the brain's ability to readily confuse and distort reality. What we perceive as obvious and what we actually believe, is complicated by our real lack of awareness regarding the complex set of clues derived from visual tasks. They join together to present dangers to the ill-prepared pilot.

No computer yet devised has the brain's processing or memory capacity. It is one of the most complex mechanisms known. You could regard it as the control and information-processing centre for virtually all human activity. The brain plays a key role in aviation human factors. It processes information about the flying environment, makes decisions, transmits signals to hands, feet and allows speech.

The brain's components

There are four major parts:

- The cerebellum is rather small and is situated just behind the top of the spinal cord. It controls balance and muscular co-ordination essential to the motor skills of physically flying the aircraft.
- The thalamus is slightly smaller and is above the cerebellum. It is a central control mechanism for messages passing to and from the sense organs. A sub-system called the hypothalamus controls body temperature and metabolism (the process of converting air and food into substances the body can use), and endocrine (hormone balance) levels, affecting mainly energy, moods and reaction to stress.
- The limbic system, is a series of canals around the thalamus. This governs emotions and any planned series of activities.
- The cerebrum, is the largest part. It accounts for all complex mental activity such as thinking, remembering things, sensory perception, and the initiation of voluntary movement. The outer cortex is connected to the sensory organs as well as motor activities such as walking, running, etc.

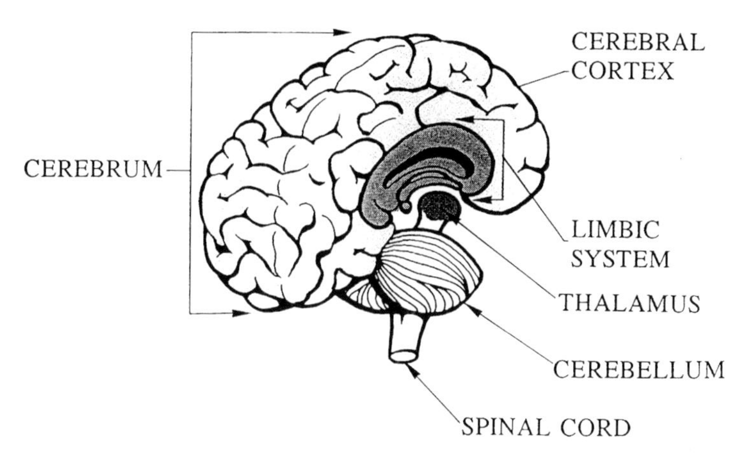

Figure 20 Main components of the brain

The cerebrum has two distinct parts, called hemispheres. Both these hemispheres oversee functions such as sensory, motor, visual and hearing. The left side handles visual input from the right side; the right side handles visual input from the left side. This pattern is the same for the majority of other left–right activities, including parts on opposite sides of the body.

What we do know is that the brain is the very heart of the body's central nervous system. This is essential for inter-communication between the various organs and the brain. The brain is regarded as the 'command centre' and dictates how different parts react. It is worth noting that in skilled psychomotor performance such as physically flying aerobatic sequences, it is thought that the signals go directly from the spinal cord to the hands and feet. This obviously does not go to the brain for normal 'processing'.

How the brain functions

The brain receives information from the eyes, ears and other sensors via tiny electrical impulses that travel through nerve fibres. A conversion process then takes place, according to what is required, meaning the dissemination of content, from what tasks the body is involved in at the time, including time relationships. All this information is then stored in the brain's memory banks through a very complex process. Some of this process has a direct effect on pilot performance.

Memory and forgetfulness

We all have short- and long-term memory. Many things (for example, complex and long ATC clearances) have to be written down, otherwise we would forget them. The short-term memory has what we call a 'high rate of decay'. Long-term memory, however, has a much slower 'decay' rate. This is considered to be in permanent storage. If the information is not used it will start to fade over time, but there is certainly research evidence to support the belief that once the information has been 'programmed' into long-term storage it will never be lost. Medical experts have had repeated success by electrically stimulating the brain in controlled experiments. Participants in many instances have clearly recalled what could only be described as 'long-forgotten personal events'. Many flight tasks are learned by repetition. After a long lay-off you do not forget how to fly, your skills are merely somewhat rusty.

Every pilot performs a whole variety of procedures, some that interfere with others. This can happen with two similar type procedures as in some flying exercises. The brain processes new information, which can interfere with information already there.

Everyone is capable of improving his or her memory. One of the best ways of doing this is to practise the various exercises and tasks which build up a ready store of information. The use of easily understood personal shorthand techniques assists in writing down ATC clearances and instructions. Checklists are also a valuable and essential *aide-mémoire*.

Mnemonics is probably the most common technique in aviation. It is like a mental shorthand that jogs the memory. In the early days of flying there were few if any formal checklists, so checks were reduced to BUMPF (brakes, undercarriage, mixture, prop pitch, fuel), which was a favourite one. There are many others. The idea was that they were pertinent and easily activated the memory.

The brain as a motivating force

How we act or behave originates from within the brain. This is a positive procedure because it motivates you to act, as opposed to relapsing into a negative stagnant state. In aviation you can be motivated to do a variety of things: practice instrument flying, flapless approaches, short-field landings and such. On the other hand you might be motivated to ensure you make safe decisions, which can bring with it a satisfying sense of responsibility. On the downside, you could also be motivated to take risks through the influence of other people's actions.

Psychologists now describe motivation in terms of 'individual needs or ambitions'. These motivating 'drives' move people to behave in certain ways. No one knows exactly where within the brain motivation is triggered, although 'triggered' it surely is; hence electrical stimulation of the hypothalamus has been found to cause a strong desire for food and drink. Many of the brain's functions are reasonably well understood, and these are very important when it comes to flying performance. In that we include thinking, memory (and forgetting), recall of information and psychomotor functions.

Human factors relationship

We are aware that the brain processes information provided by the physical senses. This information is then interpreted, allowing the pilot to take necessary physical actions. For this process to work properly and efficiently, the memory banks contained in the brain must already have been 'programmed' to enable interpretation of the signals it receives. There should be no conflict between the senses and the memory.

However, we must be aware we are dealing with the 'human element', which often has weak links in the processing chain. This affects both physical and psychological behaviour. It can result in a particular individual's senses giving out incorrect or misleading information. Like a normal computer, the brain can only provide information as good as is stored in the memory banks. A good example of this relates to instrument flying, where all external references are obscured. Only the visual sense can be relied on by the pilot. The vestibular system in the inner ear may give out signals to indicate the aircraft is turning, when in fact it is flying straight and level; the more a pilot's brain is programmed about the nature of false impressions the easier it is for the brain to decipher these spurious messages.

The sensory system

The human brain needs stimuli to function properly. In flying it is very much dependent on the sensory system, but it is essential we understand that our sensory organs are not able to detect all the important information required for flight. For example, a pilot is not able to sense the actual speed of the aircraft, but acceleration and deceleration can be sensed through our muscles, and the balance mechanism of the inner ear.

The human brain is supplied with information provided by a number of physical systems. The way these systems transmit information signals to the brain can mean misinformation is provided which can lead to the pilot making errors. It is also interesting to note that some sensory systems have a limited 'operational' range. For instance, very high pitch sounds cannot be heard by the human ear, and at certain light frequencies the human eye may not be able to detect objects. Additionally, sensory systems can vary in sensitivity from one individual to another. They also deteriorate with age as well as physical and environmental conditions.

Bodily sensations

Bodily sensations come from the five senses. In most individuals these senses are highly developed. Our sense of touch, for instance, responds immediately to something very hot through the nerve endings in the fingers. If, however, a message sent to the brain from a pilot's muscles – proprioceptive sense – is in conflict with one sent from the vestibular organ of the inner ear, the brain may become confused. This could result in incorrect actions with disastrous consequences. Therefore during flight training, pilots are taught to develop confidence (skill) by using and relying on their sense of sight, believing implicitly in the flight instruments, as in IMC and at night.

The possibility of the brain interpreting sensory information inaccurately is why point, touch, confirm then move drills are so important when dealing with an in-flight emergency. It gives the brain's communication process time to slot all the information into place, confirm the problem, then arrive at the correct action the pilot should take. When I have been conducting flight checks on pilots one frequent and common problem has occurred. It concerns the checking of cockpit (checklist) items. Pilots should at least visually check a control or instrument before operating it, but this does not always happen. During take-offs and landings pilots operate controls by touch while performing other cockpit duties. So when pilots are not actually looking at which lever or switch they are touching, a potential situation is developing for a pilot-induced emergency. The percentage risk increases while the pilot's attention is concentrated on or distracted by other tasks, i.e. communication with ATC, watching other traffic, etc.

Defining perception

Perception is derived from the visual system, in other words, a pilot's physical actions are a direct response to what he/she perceives at any particular moment. This involves the motion-sensing systems of the inner ear, and the position-sensing system involving nerve endings in the skin, muscles and joints. All these systems are informing the pilot what is happening, and the mental memory banks (stored experience skills) provide the information on what to do. The pilot physically has to be on top line, so that the sensory systems can provide the best possible response.

It is easy, though, for our perception to make a mistake through misinterpreting information being received. If we are mentally expecting one thing quite strongly, but our senses perceive something different, it is possible our anticipation can have a powerful influence on the perceptive decision. A typical perceptive misinterpretation has caused navigational errors. To avoid or minimise personal embarrassment, the pilot often refers to the problem as 'being temporarily uncertain of his position'. In fact it means the pilot has misidentified a ground feature and mentally 'interprets' the wrong position. The pilot may not become aware of this immediately, which allows the navigational error to go unnoticed, compounding the problem. This even happens to very experienced pilots from time to time.

Cognitive perception and pilot ability

The cognitive mental process of evaluating information or problems, making judgements then coming to a correct decision, is based on stored knowledge and awareness. I would point out that the pilot's ability to acquire flying skills and store knowledge does not gauge competence. Knowledge is only of value if it is put to good use. I have known skilful and knowledgeable pilots get into difficult situations where neither their undoubted ability and skill or the aircraft performance could save them. They have therefore lost their lives because they could not make good judgements and correct decisions.

Mental workload limitations

A safe pilot is one who channels his/her efforts into selective attention to the information being received. Every human has two ears, for instance, but it is difficult to listen to two messages being received at the same time, and make complete sense of them. Therefore vital information might well be missed.

In the early stages of flying training it is difficult for a student pilot to take in everything that is going on, i.e. radio communications, the position of other aircraft in the immediate vicinity, as well as struggling to fly and control the aircraft. But as experience grows and the memory banks continue to build up a reservoir of aviation data, the mental ability grows through expert instruction and training. The mental process is then able to filter out spurious non-essential information and make correct judgements. However, if a pilot becomes so 'attention set' on one task, it could exclude other important information coming in and lead to a dangerous situation developing; for example, a pilot is concentrating all his/her attention on an ILS approach in heavy IMC, keeping the localiser and glideslope needles exactly in the centre. The pilot misses the tower controller's call for a missed approach due to the runway being blocked by the preceding aircraft. With a 200ft cloudbase and reduced visibility, this situation has all the potential for a major disaster.

This sort of total attention set can easily be applied to other types of common accident scenarios. Total reliance on both audio and visual stall warnings is misplaced, the reason being (other than deliberate stall and recovery exercises during training or flight checks) that the pilot must be totally distracted for them to work, otherwise he/she would have noticed the airspeed decreasing (ASI), and the real danger of an impending stall situation. It is entirely possible that neither the aural warning nor the visual light would penetrate through the pilot's concentrated attention. (I have noticed this is particularly so when one or two annunciator panel lights are already illuminated.)

Even with all the electronic devices available to modern aviation, aircraft still continue inadvertently to stall and sometimes spin as they did in the early days. We can conclude from this that these devices, while necessary, are not totally effective in all circumstances.

Communication

One of my pet hates is pilots and controllers who do not enunciate their words properly. Verbal communication is vital to all aspects of aviation, but like everything else connected with human activity it is prone to error, distortion, interference from background noise and bad quality of transmission. Over the years this has led to a number of accidents. If I do not understand anything, I always request 'say again', or 'say again all after ______', whatever is appropriate. All pilots must remain conscious of these errors and analyse the quality of their transmissions. The main problem seems to be speaking too fast, clipped speech and incorrect phraseology, not forgetting the correct *projection* of the voice into the microphone.

CHAPTER 27
STRESS AND ITS EFFECT

The word stress implies a nervous strain or mental tension. What we should be aware of is that stress affects us all.

Unlike aircraft where the maximum stress factors are known, pilot stress is somewhat more complex, therefore the demands placed on it by the pilot or the environment must not exceed the capacity to perform correctly. It is important to realise that it isn't how much stress we face, but how we handle it that determines its effect on us.

Each of us has his own definition of stress. We encounter stressful situations wherever we go. One of the most recently publicised chronic forms of stress is road rage. In any event, stress is certainly an integral part of our everyday lives. There are even circumstances where some stress is desirable to achieve 'peak performance', for instance sporting activities, and certainly in military flight operations it helps to keep situational awareness on top line because of the intense challenges being faced. It is not uncommon to hear the expression 'adrenaline junkies' used to describe those who thrive on some stress.

Problems start when we become overloaded by stress. All physical and mental activity needs energy. Therefore energy fuels human performance. Stress uses up energy in our human fuel tank at a vast rate, leaving only a small amount to meet our other needs.

Stressors

The stimulus for stress is known as the stressor. Stress is produced by a great many factors, and these vary from person to person. We can narrow them down to fall under three broad headings:

- work (productive and unproductive)
- physical problems
- personal profile

Productive work versus stress

Productive work has a precise purpose. For a pilot, productive work means those tasks which directly contribute to accomplishing a flight. This means flight planning, working out performance data, flying the aircraft and post-flight duties. There are also factors that contribute to a higher crew workload. It can be bad weather, a tight operational schedule, problems with aircraft serviceability and decisions relating to performance. Of course the speed of modern aircraft is another example which has increased stress potential for pilots. This has made things happen faster in the cockpit, and leaves less margin for error.

Unproductive work versus stress

Unproductive work has no *perceived* purpose, and makes no *direct* contribution to a flight. Some examples include weather delays, military operational (mission) delays, civil airline or GA flight delays for a variety of reasons, maintenance problems, unnecessary paperwork (it happens everywhere), and 'passenger' delays. Unproductive work builds up frustration stressors producing emotional strains. This mental-emotional stress can easily exceed that produced by the physical exertion of actually flying. These frustrations can produce individual, personal and inter-personal stress which can filter through to affect sleep and appetite.

To start to cope both mentally and emotionally with productive and unproductive work stressors, they have to be understood in the context of each task they relate to. Then they can be tackled and minimised individually.

Physical problems versus stress

We are now aware that any form of work produces stress, which shows itself in a form of fatigue. This in effect is a physical problem. Samples of physical problems that produce stress are fatigue, excessive noise (as in the cockpits of some aircraft), heat and cold, illness, poor diet, dehydration and age (which reduces the tolerance to other forms of stress). There are obvious chemical examples too – alcohol, narcotics, even prescribed drugs. Any stress that affects our physical well-being reduces our efficiency and proficiency as pilots.

Personal problems versus stress

These are mainly psychological in nature. For instance, the effect of family and financial difficulties can be very debilitating and can quickly build up high levels of stress. They also increase vulnerability to depression and anxiety, and produce a low threshold of control. If a pilot has personal problems that are allowed to go unchecked, they can have a detrimental effect on flight safety. Accidents in aviation often occur because the task requirements exceed the pilot's capabilities; this is more likely to occur when the pilot brings his/her 'ground stress' into the cockpit.

Defining stress

Stress is the word we use to describe how the body reacts to the various demands placed on it. We know that stress uses energy, which then reduces the amount available for a pilot to perform effectively. One of the main problems is the individual's ability to cope with one form of stress while being subjected to other 'stressors'.

Each individual reacts differently to stress, because each one of us has a different mental and physical make-up. The analysis of stress is further complicated due to the intricate mental make-up of the human mind. By this I mean that an event that produces stress one day may not have the same, if any, effect the next day. Differences in stress can often be related to an individual's frame of mind. Differences in attitude, personality and experience considerably influence our ability to cope with stress. A basic understanding of the effects of stress makes you better able to cope with it. There is a three-stage response to stress by our bodies:

Alert reaction This is the initial stage in which the body realises it is being subjected to stress, and prepares to do battle, or retreat, according to the mental make-up of the individual. The body releases hormones, which speeds up the heartbeat and breathing and raises the blood sugar level. This triggers a sudden increase in energy and muscular strength, with keener vision and hearing. It is the sort of reaction that can occur during a sudden encounter with turbulence, or when dealing with a difficult cross-wind landing.

Resistance reaction When the body starts to repair any 'stress damage'. This process helps it to cope with some longer-term stressors such as extreme heat or cold, even a sustained physical effort. If the stress continues (as on a long flight in bad weather, then a diversion to another airport), the body will endeavour to sustain its state of higher readiness.

Fatigue and exhaustion In most cases this is a temporary state and affects specific parts of the body. Pilots who fly for long duty periods experience tiredness and different levels of exhaustion, depending on their age and physical state. After a good rest they recover and are ready for the next flight.

If the body's resistance and advancing exhaustion continues without respite over a long period, serious physical damage can be done. In severe cases this can result in death. Whatever the source of stress, failure to manage it depletes the individual's reservoir of energy. This leads to poor judgement, eroded performance and a loss of alertness. This can result in the misreading of maps, charts and checklists, loss of time perception, straying off course, even the misjudgement of distance and altitude. Some of the main signs I use to recognise high stress levels in pilots are:

- inattention to briefings
- continual yawning
- pale complexion and red-rimmed eyes (often bloodshot)
- slowed/inappropriate reactions
- a tendency to complain about almost anything – accommodation, food, etc.
- a tendency to skip over or miss checklist items
- sleeping or nodding off at the slightest opportunity

CHAPTER 28
STRESS MANAGEMENT

Coping with stress is largely up to the individual. There are no instant cures. Many stress-related problems can be tackled by exercising common sense; other solutions may involve an individual changing lifelong habits. This is not only very difficult, but may prove impossible.

In general terms, maintaining a positive mental attitude can form the basis from which to tackle stress. We must try to eliminate, or at least control, the worst stressors that affect us. Better planning of our personal schedule can help. Attention to our own physical and psychological well-being is another way we can help ourselves; so is a review of our job performance. A sort of DIY common sense assistance kit will put us on the right road to dealing with the stress that affects us.

Our mental performance will affect our flying performance. Therefore it is important to:

- be positive and tackle your responsibilities and problems as and when they occur. Avoid putting off things in the hope that they will automatically sort themselves out. It doesn't happen in the real world.
- avoid indulging in hopeful fantasy. Take a positive attitude and help things to work out.
- avoid making promises you cannot keep. Do not over-commit yourself. Failure to keep promises (for normal people) can be a real source of stress.
- try to be more relaxed and flexible. Develop a better sociable attitude towards others. (Good inter-personal relationships can solve many stress-related problems.)
- have a general good sense of humour – it helps to lessen stress.

Look after your health. As a pilot it is a necessity if you are to maintain the validity of your pilot's licence. Therefore:

- moderate (or stop) smoking, and limit the drinking of alcohol
- relax when the opportunity occurs
- eat regularly and avoid missing meals (very difficult, I know, in the 'pressured' aviation environment of a long duty day)
- take regular physical exercise; even deep breathing for short periods helps to lessen stress

- give yourself plenty of time to get to the airport – if possible avoid the frustrations of rush-hour traffic
- do not allow unforeseen events or delays to wind up your stress level; there is almost certainly nothing you could have done to avoid it anyway

I am as aware as any aviator that it is difficult to follow some of the above suggestions, but try nevertheless.

Additional related stress

When we fly, how 'emotional' we feel can have a tremendous effect on our personal ability to perform properly, especially when it comes to judgement. It is the pressure of time that affects almost all of us. These pressures are never more evident than when flying an aircraft. In flying every aircrew member has to perform a number of tasks simultaneously, and every one of these elements takes up a certain amount of time. Unfortunately, the time-task demands frequently exceed the available time, which leads to overloading. This results in the stress response increasing sharply and possibly reaching a dangerously high level.

Most aircrew have a good sense of time and are able to operate efficiently, thus gaining a measure of job satisfaction. If, however, the time pressures exceed what can reasonably be accomplished comfortably, the individual is liable to feel 'time threatened'. The problem then revolves around time for recovery. Periods of over-stressing lead to physical reactions such as indigestion, headaches, irritability stressors surfacing and, of course, impaired judgement.

Corporate flying stressors

A favourite stressor with which I am very familiar occurs frequently in corporate flying. The passengers, who are usually company executives, have a bad tendency to turn up late for a prearranged flight departure time. They complain if they are delayed even further, because of ATC and/or IFR slot departure times being cancelled, then having to be rearranged. Internal company memos highlighting this problem sometimes have a short-term effect for the better, but basically remain the same unless real awareness and an executive directive is forthcoming from the top. The frustrating part is, those same passengers *know* they would miss a commercial flight in the same circumstances.

The worst-case scenario is the corporate executive with a pilot licence who wants to fly the company aircraft. The problem here is obvious: he/she has divided attention, among other problems. The worst part is if the pilot-executive is low-time and basically unqualified, or untrained, for that type of flying. It is a bad idea to take any responsibility for flying the company's own aircraft after a hard day of business meetings for a whole variety of psychological and physiological reasons. We are actually looking at a flight safety problem, which is then multiplied because the 'regular company pilot' is under greater stress in monitoring, coping with possible bad weather, and an emergency if one occurs.

We must *always* bear in mind the influence emotions can have on our ability to perform well. The following true story of a near corporate disaster illustrates the dangers. An experienced pilot was hired by a major company to fly their Beech Super Kingair B200. What the pilot did not know was that the managing director liked to fly the Kingair himself whenever he could. He used it like a taxi to fly around Europe. During the first week the new pilot was flying to a destination on the Dutch coast prone to low cloud and bad visibility. On that particular flight the airport was below minimums, but the managing director wanted his pilot to press on and 'make an approach anyway', motivated by perceived or actual business pressures. They could already hear on the radio that other aircraft were diverting. The new pilot did not want to be forced into making an approach, so he over-ruled the MD and made an immediate decision to divert safely to an alternative. On the ground, waiting for the weather to lift, the MD realised he had made a bad decision and had tried to force that bad decision on the legal captain of the aircraft.

Recognising warning stressors

Extreme time pressures can lead to excessive overload. To help alleviate this each individual must learn to quickly identify personal warning signs that will help reduce the stress. It is advantageous to be aware of the main symptoms of excessive stress, or stress overload:

- trying to do too many things at once
- eating too fast
- never seeming to have enough time to complete tasks
- general impatience and frustration with others who you perceive are doing things too slowly
- talking too quickly
- making plans for a range of activities for which there is no reasonable time available
- driving too fast on the road (especially to and from work)
- little or no time for relaxation, inter-personal relationships (marital, family,

etc.), or for generally 'catching up' with an enjoyable lifestyle (quality of life)
- hate wasting time personally, but particularly when others do it

If you recognise any of these symptoms you could have *excessive stress overload*. I'm not meaning to imply you are in the advanced stages of distress, because each individual handles stress in different ways. Some individuals and family groups lead naturally fast-paced lives with lots of activities. Many can handle this faster life, others can adjust to it. In aviation you can quickly start to lose track of important operational tasks, and this can increase the chance of making mistakes and jeopardising safety.

Results of poor chain decisions (PCD)

If we analyse accident data we will see that most accidents and incidents do not result from one really bad decision, but from a chain of smaller, poor decisions which are not individually critical by themselves.

What we are talking about here is when one poor decision increases the possibility of another, then another. As the PCD chain increases, the chances of the flight reaching its destination safely diminish in direct proportion to the total number of poor decisions. Errors or flight problems increase the workload which unconsciously makes the stress level rise.

Excessive stress can also be the product of longer-term problems. Curing these will usually be long-term as well, which needs self-discipline and patience. Try to develop new skills and make new friends with new outlooks. Be more tolerant towards others. Instead of confrontation (which produces stressors of a severe nature), use negotiating techniques and assertiveness to control your work schedule and the demands on your time. Co-operative tolerance towards a (stressed) chief pilot, for instance, can often defuse a bad situation. Be careful, though, to seek to change only those things you *reasonably* can influence, and tolerate and accept those you cannot. Recognising your own limitations in all of this will go a long way to being successful.

Summary

- the effects of stress are cumulative
- any stressful situation that develops in the aircraft, or is related to it, compounds the problem(s) if moderate to extreme stress is already present
- as stress increases task overload can be rapid, and the individual's ability to cope with this situation will be severely affected
- when suffering from severe stress you are more likely to make bad decisions;

for instance, pressing on in bad weather because of commercial scheduling pressures, accepting aircraft technical problems that should be fixed, and so on
- stress can increase insidiously to the point that it is impossible to cope
- there is no magic formula for managing stress, but it will help to take an overall 'common sense' approach, and endeavour to tackle realistically each stressor in the various areas of your life one by one

From our review of the subject we can see that stress affects everyone to a greater or lesser extent, dependent on our individual lifestyle. Face it and make it a priority objective to know how to minimise and overcome it. To give you a better idea of how much stress there is in your life, listed below are the top ten most stressful events. The more change you have in your life the more stress you will experience. Therefore it follows that there can be a marked change in personal health in the short to medium term (up to two years).

- divorce
- death of a close family member
- marital separation (even for a short period)
- trouble with the law (going to court or, even worse, a jail term)
- getting married
- illness or suffering a restricting injury
- losing your job (dismissed or redundant)
- worries over health of an immediate family member
- sexual difficulties

Remember that each of us has a different stress-coping capability, so it doesn't necessarily follow that you will automatically get ill or sick if you experience a number of the above list over a short period of time. Try to avoid exceeding your own limit by knowing the warning signs from your body.

CHAPTER 29
RISK ASSESSMENT

Including Military Operations

There is no situation in life that can be considered 'risk free'. Indeed, the majority of the accidents that occur happen in the home, in what most people consider a *low-risk* environment.

So we can see from this that some risk exists in most human activity, and as we gradually mature it is accepted as part of everyday life. In fact it becomes a fundamental part of human behaviour and an integral part of our psychological make-up. Therefore we have the inbuilt ability to recognise risk, assess how to deal with it and make a decision. Which means that risk influences our decision-making. When we come to consider aviation and add to this the high-stress military element, then we are dealing with a far more complex risk situation. Let's look at this in two parts as it is very important.

Firstly, no one is born with the ability to fly. How often have you heard one of the standard excuses for someone (when pressed) for not wanting to learn to fly – 'If God had wanted me to fly, then He would have given me a pair of wings when I was born!' In fact, this is simply an individual's built-in risk assessment working overtime without understanding or having due consideration of all the facts. Naturally we all accept that only a small percentage of men and women will want to learn to fly anyway.

As in any other skilled occupation, flying can only be learned through education, meaning practical instruction and theoretical study, and practice, being the steady build-up of experience over a period of time. When motor skills (physically flying the aircraft with all the integral parts that go with it) have been acquired, then the development of more complex judgements based on a multiple number of factors can be developed. This involves more abstract judgements using intelligence and awareness.

Pilot performance (risk)

This can be affected in many ways, both before and during a flight involving a high degree of (military) risk when stress levels are high.

- Physical stress, which concerns the pilot's immediate environment which can affect his/her physical state. This can be high/low temperatures, humidity, noise levels, or lack of oxygen for higher than normal cruise altitudes (as in mountainous regions).
- Physiological stress, relating to the pilot's actual physical condition, i.e. debilitating fatigue, inadequate diet, living in uncomfortable temporary shelter (against a background of impending military danger), etc.
- Psychological stress, involving an emotional state of mind. The need to plan/navigate accurately, and assess a changing situation in what might be a hostile environment, communicate with a military unit on the aircraft, and cope with the responsibility of flying (the task force) safely in and out of the target area. The additional stress of decisions involving life and death.
- Sociological stress, meaning personal emotional stress as a result of family problems, financial, etc.

When we look at these stress factors as a whole they can seriously jeopardise any flight, easily doubling the risk of an entire operation. You are, or should be, well aware of your own psychological profile and experience limitations. What you also have to be certain of are the capabilities of those you recruit. That only comes through experience. I have tried and tested colleagues I use, who have proved themselves in such operations.

Aircraft (risk)

The main risk factors concerning the aircraft involve its suitability for the task and the technical (plus equipment) condition and serviceability. The other important consideration is fuel. This does not simply mean filling up the tanks before each flight. Proper fuel calculations must be completed. These include the fuel required for the actual flight, sufficient for diversion, plus holding and a contingency reserve. However, we must not forget that fuel calculations should also be made during the flight to ensure that fuel burn versus time is being consumed according to the flight plan. Pilots consider 'fuel planning' during the pre-flight phase, but they do not always understand it is an important part of the overall risk assessment. With military operations, additional fuel contingency plans are vital to cope with the unexpected diversion/delay/rerouting, etc. not encountered in normal civilian flying.

Environment

Environment concerns a wide-ranging risk element, and includes situations which could restrict or alter the pilot's decisions. This could mean the actual or anticipated weather, and operational considerations of operating in adverse terrain.

Time has a direct influence on the main elements. Time (overall or short-term) can easily be overlooked in flight by a pilot, which you might think incredible during quiet reflection on the ground without other distractions. It can easily happen when a pilot/crew is totally involved in resolving/dealing with a single or combination of flight problems. Time can then in a sense become an enemy, and lead to rash or incorrect decisions being made under (perceived or real) pressure. It can be said, therefore, that risk is multiplied in direct proportion to the decrease (shortness) in time.

The factors mentioned here are part of every flight. Each can affect the flight individually, separately, or join together to make a larger, or perceived greater risk. Having said all this, it is obvious that to assess risk it must first be recognised and acknowledged. Certain risks in aviation, though, are not recognised. This is through lack of awareness or knowledge. Hazardous situations can easily and quickly develop because of this. There is no printed formula for instructing pilots *how* to recognise and evaluate the degree of risk they are taking, because human behaviour and situations vary so widely in different types of flight operations.

Complacency and over-confidence

A reduced lack of danger awareness can lead to complacency and over-confidence. I've noted that this tendency often develops in quite experienced pilots who have flown in many different regions of the world without mishap, or who have not had to face real problems. Although the successful pilot must have confidence in both himself and his equipment, pilots' levels of confidence are a result of their past experiences and training. Personality make-up also plays a major part.

In a normal civil general aviation situation, a pilot's learning curve in repetitive flight schedules or flying a new aircraft type levels out. Decision-making becomes easier and the flying routine almost automatic. With military operations, each one is different and presents a new set of challenges, so complacency or over-confidence should be eradicated.

Complacency can easily set in when stress has been overcome. Complacency leads to a lessening of situational awareness and a gradual decline in proficiency brought about by boredom, hence the higher accident rate for pilots with 500 hours or so (who think they are experienced but aren't, and overstep their experience limits). I have found this when instructing mid-rank military pilots who have tasted executive authority without the responsibility of real 'operational' decision-making outside the training environment. A pilot with a bad behavioural attitude will usually do things on the basis of trying to prove that he is better than anyone else. He takes risks to achieve his object, as proof not only to himself, but to others that his way is the best. It seldom is.

Risk shifting

Do not be influenced by others who have less regard for the risks than you do. Group conformity, or the resignation of individuals to go along with the decisions made by others, often leads to the acceptance of unreasonable and unsafe requests. This compliance shows under-confidence and lack of pilot-in-command ability. Irrespective of whether an individual has an attitude of conformity or resignation, great care must be taken when agreeing to a group decision. This is because it is often made on a basis of compromise between the stronger (more assertive) individuals in the group. It is a strong possibility that these individuals may be inclined to take greater risks than others (a detrimental influence on overall group decisions).

Chapter 30

Mayday – All Four Engines Have Failed!

Resourcefulness, training and good cockpit management techniques saved a £34 million disaster and the lives of 247 passengers on BA009 over West Java on 24 June 1982.

The Boeing 747 was *en route* from the UK to New Zealand, but on that particular leg of the flight they were heading for Perth in Western Australia. What the crew were unaware of was that the Galunggung volcano in West Java had erupted violently only ninety minutes before BA009 flew into the area. A dense cloud of volcanic ash had billowed high into the night sky.

Captain Eric Moody was away from the flight deck as the drama began to unfold. It was 2040 hours when Roger Greaves, the first officer, began to notice green sparks of static electricity speckling the windscreen. The flight engineer, Barry Townley-Freeman, was startled when he looked out of a side window and saw the starboard engines lit up as though magnesium flares were burning inside the cowlings. Captain Moody returned at that moment and discovered that the engines on his side were also ablaze with light. It was the eeriest thing he had seen in his airline career. By this time smoke was beginning to thicken in the passenger cabin below.

As the captain was considering what to do next, the 747 started to swing, then the flight engineer called out, 'Engine failure, number four,' and thirty seconds later, 'number two has gone – so has number three. I don't believe it, we've lost the lot!'

Captain Moody turned left and started to head north towards Java and the closest diversion airport, Djakarta, which was 120 miles away. First Officer Greaves transmitted the emergency call on the radio: 'Mayday, Mayday, Mayday. Speedbird 009, we've lost all four engines.'

Passengers prayed as the 747 suddenly started to descend at 5,000 feet per minute. Then heavy St Elmo's fire, smoke and volcanic dust was suddenly present in the cockpit.

As the Boeing began its long descent from 37,000 feet, the immediate reaction on the flight deck was, 'What have we done wrong?' The crew were well aware that the few previous cases of four engines failing on a modern passenger jet had been due to mismanagement of the anti-icing or fuel systems. But on 009 everything was on and normal – the official checklists had been meticulously followed. The only option open to the crew at that stage was the full engine restart drill they had all practised in the 747 flight simulator at Heathrow. Captain Moody and his first officer knew that, in theory, the altitude at which air density best favours restarting a Rolls-Royce RB211 engine is 28,000 feet. In each of the simulated practices (LOFT training) the engines had started up at that height. But this had been on the ground; this was the real thing at altitude. So now they started the relight drill. However, whatever they tried, nothing happened.

Unburned fuel spilled from the engines and passengers saw them begin to trail orange flame. The wasted fuel was being set on fire as it was thrown out of the jet pipes. Losing altitude fast, the 747 passed through 28,000 feet and there was no sign of an engine start. At 26,000 feet a warning horn shattered the silence. Without engine power the pressurisation system had failed. The three flight-deck crew grabbed their full-face oxygen masks, but the first officer's malfunctioned. Although Captain Moody needed to conserve every bit of height he could, he did not want his co-pilot passing out through oxygen starvation at such a critical time, so he increased the rate of descent to 8,000 feet per minute. At 20,000 feet Roger Greaves finally managed to get his oxygen mask to work, and the captain eased off on the rate of descent. In the passenger cabin the yellow oxygen masks had deployed from their overhead stowage points. One female passenger, Pearl Jepson, seeing row after row of people wearing the masks, felt she was watching an air disaster film. The only difference was that no one panicked.

Djakarta airport was now only eighty miles ahead, but was situated on the far side of 10,000-foot mountains which the 747 had no hope of clearing. The passengers were briefed by the cabin attendants for ditching.

As they were passing 13,000 feet, Captain Moody saw that the engines no longer glowed, but they were still dead. It was a nerve-racking time, because in about six minutes they would have to ditch into the sea in total darkness. The biggest problem was, nobody had ever done it before.

The crew had no intention of giving up and once again tried to start the engines. There was a flicker of movement on one of the engine gauges, and after an agonising few moments number four engine started, and eighty seconds later number three obliged. Then one and two came in almost together. It was the sweetest sound the crew had ever heard. Their crew teamwork and purposeful tenacity had worked perfectly throughout the traumatic emergency. But the problems were far from over.

As they descended further towards Djakarta the number two engine began to backfire continuously and had to be shut down. It seemed a long descent into Djakarta, and when they reached 2,000 feet and began the approach, the crew realised they had lost virtually all forward visibility. They could hardly see the runway lights. Added to that, the ILS glideslope for runway 24 was unserviceable. With considerable back-up assistance from his crew, the captain managed to keep a reasonable approach profile. He found he could see marginally better by bending sideways and looking through the outer four inches of the windscreen. BA009 finally made a safe landing a bare forty minutes after all four engines had stopped.

Engineers had to chip away black volcanic deposits from all four engines' turbine blades. The leading edges of the wings were stripped of paint as if they had been sandblasted. The windscreen was opaque. The local Boeing representative told the crew it was the most severely damaged 747 to have kept flying. The volcanic ash cloud from Galunggung had snuffed out the Boeing's engines like sand thrown on a fire. Only in clean air below the ash cloud had restarting been possible.

Apart from the enthusiastic thanks of all the passengers, Captain Eric Moody and his crew received special commendations from British Airways and a presentation dinner from grateful underwriters at Lloyd's. It was their £34 million liability for the aircraft had there been a crash, with many more millions for passengers who would undoubtedly have died.

For Captain Moody personally there have been many honours, notably an award from The Guild of Air Pilots and Air Navigators for outstanding airmanship. But there is a special place in his UK home for a handsome pewter dish given to him by his crew on BA009. It is inscribed: *Eric. Thanks are not enough, BA009, 24th June 1982.*

I would like to add my own congratulations: *well done!*

CHAPTER 31

'SO WHAT *REALLY* HAPPENED?'

Air accident investigators are paid to ask questions, but do they ask the right ones, and, more importantly, do they get the right answers? In many cases the answer to that is no.

People seldom tell the truth, we are all aware of that, but in many instances when major air accidents have happened, the airlines, regulatory bodies, even governments, display a long list of human errors, gross incompetence and indecision in dealing with the real issues of the accident cause.

Investigators made extensive enquiries after the Air New Zealand DC-10 crashed into Mount Erebus in the Antarctic. It was on a sightseeing trip from Auckland so passengers could see the wonderful panoramic views. The round trip was eleven hours – no problem for the DC-10. One of the main problems for a flight of that nature was if the aircraft developed a technical problem, because there was nowhere to divert to. Down near the South Pole, conventional navigation is impossible. Inertial navigation is used.

Just a perfunctory check of the aircraft equipment records shows the almost unbelievable fact that there were no Arctic survival kits on the DC-10, certainly an incredible situation as they were, and had been, operating over one of the most inhospitable and dangerous regions of the world. The flight records also revealed that none of the crew, neither captain nor first officer, had flown the route before. Also the weather changes from good to *very* bad in a very short space of time were notorious. Nothing shows that any of the crews on Air New Zealand's series of sightseeing flights was ever briefed about route or destination area weather conditions. The other big weather danger was if a 'whiteout' occurred. (The author is very familiar with this phenomenon from flight operations in the northern Arctic. This results in a complete loss of depth perception, which means a pilot cannot separate the sky from the surface.)

The worst error was that the wrong navigational data for the Antarctic flight had been programmed into the INS computer, which in effect placed the DC-10 on a track for Mount Erebus. Unfortunately the weather deteriorated, radio reception became difficult, and the final disastrous saga took place. The captain decided to make a VFR descent to 1,500 feet using the incorrectly programmed INS. The INS had in fact moved their programmed course twenty-five miles to the east, right in line with Mount Erebus. As they were so low all the flight-deck crew members were trying to navigate visually, and were looking for ground features that would be visible along what they thought was the correct track. In point of fact, the features that could be seen were very similar to those along the correct track, so it was easy to misidentify and mislead the pilots. There was no thought in their minds they could be on a collision course with Mount Erebus.

The visibility dropped to whiteout conditions and the DC-10 collision with Erebus resulted, and 257 people were killed. Almost immediately after the accident the cover-up by the airline management and senior pilots started, with everyone fighting to protect their names and reputations. The captain was blamed for the accident by the New Zealand accident investigation authority. The case was fought all the way to the British Privy Council and the crew was finally cleared of blame. The Law Lords gave a significant and damning summation: 'It is an understandable weakness on the part of the individual members of the airline management to shrink from acknowledging, even to themselves, that something they had done – or failed to do – might have been the cause of so horrendous an accident.'

The other 'international accident' that caused far-reaching repercussions was when the Russians shot down Korean Airlines Flight 007, a Boeing 747 carrying 246 passengers. The aircraft was over the dangerous Kamchatka Peninsula *en route* to Seoul in South Korea. It happened in 1983 when Ronald Reagan was US President and the Cold War had not yet ended. There was furious international reaction, not least in the White House, where the President and his staff of high-powered advisers badly mishandled the whole affair. It soon became apparent that the Russians had thought KAL007 was a suspicious intruder entering a sensitive military area. Washington clammed up, including spokesmen from the National Security Council. American political hawks clamoured for a showdown with the Russians, and President Reagan closed Aeroflot offices in Washington and New York. A sixty-day ban was also proposed on all flights to Russia. There were bitter international exchanges, accusations and political wrangling, and a well-orchestrated cover-up of all the events surrounding the tragedy.

As it later came to light from expert testimony (and intelligence reports), the Russians themselves had been involved in a long list of incompetence, human errors and 'higher (military) authority cover-ups' caused by a breakdown, or lack, of proper military contingency planning. Again, this boiled down to a 'tragedy that was going to happen sooner or later' – a comment from a senior Russian fighter pilot based in the area.

Various reasons for KAL007 straying into Russian airspace have been put forward. One is that the wrong data were put into the INS. Another concerned a tight company fuel policy, in which crews were pressured to make such drastic fuel savings that safety margins were compromised. One report even said the captain was working for the CIA and was *asked* to over-fly the area; another that the crew was incompetent. All are highly improbable for a whole variety of logical reasons. The end analysis shows, however, that the real truth may well be buried in some top secret intelligence file, Russian or American. The problem is that no one is in a position, or more likely has the will, to find out.

What *was* a frightening theory was written in the official International Civil Aviation Organisation (ICAO) report. This puts forward the idea that the Inertial Navigation System, INS, had been programmed with about a ten-degree track error. The ICAO report stated: 'This presumes a considerable degree of lack of attention on the part of the entire flightcrew, but not to a degree that is unknown in international civil aviation.' This is certainly a damning indictment of all aircrew throughout the world. In any case, it is certainly not true. I think ICAO need to do a little soul-searching themselves, being the international body which helps to formulate and advise on policy and regulations for civil aviation. But as with all these organisations it will not happen because (like the Air New Zealand management after the DC-10 Mount Erebus crash), no official will take any responsibility for putting forward real solutions. It will simply result in obscure reports and speeches paying only lip service to the real issue that should be tackled: minimising human error.

Eventually, and inevitably of course, the tragic episode of KAL007 was put down to human error, although by whom has not been made clear.

The other side of the coin in many air emergencies shows that aircrew have displayed a considerable amount of technical skill, fortitude and courage in overcoming dangerous situations. One particular incident epitomises how pilots can react and pull off amazing feats of airmanship in moments of crisis. In 1983, an Air Canada Boeing 767 amazingly ran out of fuel at 41,000 feet on a flight from Montreal to Edmonton. It appears there had been confusion between weighing fuel in kilograms and pounds.

The captain and first officer pulled off a magnificent and safe forced landing without power. They not only received Certificates of Merit from the Canadian Airline Pilots' Association, but outstanding Airmanship Awards from the FAI. Unfortunately, the Air Canada internal company investigation blamed the captain and first officer, together with two refuelling personnel.

The union, press and public outcry was so strong, it forced the Canadian government into holding an Independent Board of Inquiry. This resulted in both the pilots and refuellers not only being exonerated, but praised – the pilots in particular for their courageous efforts. What the Board did say was that corporate (Air Canada) administration and technical equipment deficiencies were overcome by the skill and professionalism of the flightcrew (including flight attendants). It was the Board's conclusion that a major disaster had been avoided. The Board chairman also talked about 'the alarming evidence in failure of communications at all levels of Air Canada's corporate structure. This was of great concern in an industry that was responsible for so many lives every day.'

What we can say at this stage of the new technological revolution and new-generation aircraft is that errors will continue and accidents will happen. But if responsible members of the aviation community make the effort, then we can further improve the performance of cockpit crews and overall flight safety.

AUTHOR'S POSTSCRIPT

We have to keep in mind at all times that flying is about people, pilots like you and me. It is certainly about the human factor element more than machines. Everything in aviation has been designed and operated by people. Even the NASA Space Shuttles would not be the same without people. Therefore, how people think and act influences the success of the system. Many factors can affect your performance as a pilot, or in any other flightcrew member position. Sometimes it can be for the better, such as well-conducted and efficient training; then sometimes there is a downside, so we must be aware of both so that it will ultimately make us safer.

* * *

> There are in man's actions neither rewards nor punishments,
> there are simply *consequences*.
>
> Robert G. Ingersol

General Questionnaire

The subject matter for these questions has been taken at random from the material in this book. They are simply designed to help you to collect your thoughts and review the subject matter at leisure, or discuss any points raised with flightcrew colleagues.

1. What is the real objective of CRM training?
2. List the qualities of a good leader.
3. Can you describe the basic principles of conflict resolution?
4. What are the best ways of promoting good teamwork?
5. List the most important factors of good cockpit communication.
6. How would you define judgement?
7. Why is understanding stress so important to pilots?
8. Briefly describe two types of stress.
9. Why is the right mental attitude so important to flight safety?
10. Make up your own 'checklist' of '*Am I fit to fly?*'
11. Describe the four types of hypoxia and their causes.
12. What are the causes of physical stress, and how does this affect your flying ability?
13. How do the two types of memory function?
14. What are the advantages of checklists?
15. How can differences in runway slope and width affect the *perception* of your approach? Describe them.
16. What are the reasons for saying that it is dangerous to trust your sense of orientation when flying in solid IFR (in clouds)?
17. We hear a great deal about cockpit design. Discuss why it is important in preventing pilot errors.
18. Why are the mental aspects of flying considered to be more important than the physical ones?
19. What are the real advantages of flight simulators?
20. Define pilot error.
21. What is Advocacy?
22. What degrades Maximum Workload Capacity?
23. Describe Task Loading.
24. List the four major categories of Flight Resources.
25. What are Human Factors?

26. Draw a Concept Map.
27. Define Cockpit Resource Management.
28. List the five Decide Technique elements.
29. What is the first aspect of communication?
30. Describe the two main types of judgement.
31. How does invulnerability affect flight safety?
32. What are the top ten stressors?
33. Describe Structured Practice.
34. Argue for and against a Type-A person in an aviation management position.

Cockpit Resource Management

1. What is the leadership role in CRM?
2. What are the best ways of resolving conflicts in the cockpit?
3. List the important qualities of a good team leader.
4. List the five main factors in good communication.
5. How does being a good listener help team co-operation?

Management of Flight Resources

1. Describe one instance in which you demonstrated effective integration and management of a number of different flight resources.
2. Describe two human resources that you routinely use. Name at least one available human resource you haven't considered before.
3. What are your most common sources of operational information? Briefly discuss any additional sources of operational information that might be of value to you.
4. Name two pieces of equipment in your aircraft you use well. Is there any equipment you feel you could utilise better?
5. List instances where you could have better utilised various consumable resources.
6. Give instances that could have caused a deterioration of your maximum workload capacity in recent months.

Use and Function of Checklists

1. What is the general opinion of the pilots in your company regarding the use of checklists?

2. How do you pace the checklist to ensure its completion with minimum interference to other flight duties?
3. Does your company operations department set a specific policy for the use of checklists by flight crew members? If so, what is it?
4. If there were no policy, what procedures would you use?
5. How do you deal with checklist interruptions?
6. During an aircraft abnormal or emergency condition, what priority do you give to the cockpit activities?

Coping With the Future

1. Do you see current aircraft design being compatible with man's ability to work with automated machine technology?
2. Does man control machines (the aircraft) better than automated machines? List for and against.
3. What are the main advantages of automation?
4. How do you think designers should view the human element (the pilot) in the cockpit of the future?

Human Capabilities

1. What do you understand by 'pilot error'?
2. What are the most common causes of aircraft accidents?
3. What are human factors?
4. What are the main factors that influence *good* decision-making?

Cockpit Distractions

1. What procedure do you use to ensure all checklist items are completed if an interruption occurs (radio, conflicting traffic, etc.)?
2. How do you plan the 'flight tasks' to ensure minimum distraction?
3. Does your Operations Department help to reduce non-operational distractions? If so, how?
4. What have been the main distractions that have interfered with your performance of routine tasks in the cockpit?
5. How do you minimise and cope with non-operational distractions (i.e. passengers, catering, problems over live animals, etc.)?
6. What do you consider to be the main psychological pressures within the cockpit environment?

7. What physiological distractions have significantly affected your ability to perform cockpit tasks?

   To assist in answering this question, fill in the blanks:
   I forgot to .... because I was distracted by ....

Stress management

1. What noticeable signs of stress do you look out for in:
   a) Yourself?
   b) Others (crew members)?
2. Write down any method you use to deal with stress before flight and during flight.
3. If you are involved in long flights, how do you stay alert?
4. Can you give examples of when your diet or amount of rest has increased your stress level?
5. How do you ensure adequate diet and rest during busy flight operations?
6. How do you exercise?
7. Are there ways in which you consider you could improve your physical condition?
8. Does your Operations Department increase or reduce stress factors in your 'flying environment'?
9. Why is it important to understand stress?
10. Name three types of stress and list how to overcome them.
11. How does stress affect flight safety?
12. What is resistance reaction in relation to stress?
13. What effect does severe stress have on your health?
14. How do we recognise warning stressors?
15. Briefly define stress.

Glossary of Terms and Useful Definitions

ACCIDENT An occurrence directly associated with the operation of an aircraft, in which the occurrence takes place between the time anyone boards the aircraft with the intention of flight and when they disembark, and during which time any person suffers serious injury, death, or the aircraft sustains substantial damage.

AIR TRAFFIC CONTROL A service provided by the Civil Aviation Authority of each country to promote the safe, orderly and expeditious flow of air traffic.

AIRCRAFT SIMULATOR A reproduction in every respect of a specific aircraft-type flight deck. This includes all controls, instruments, necessary equipment and systems panels. It is purely ground-based, but has both visual and full motion capability.

ADVOCACY Refers to the need to state what you know or believe in a forthright manner. It means not only stating your position, but maintaining your position until completely convinced by the facts, not the authority of the other person, that it is wrong. (There are many examples of airline accidents in which other crew members may have had the correct answer, as indicated by the questioning of the actions of the captain. However, they did not advocate their position strongly enough, or capitulated to the authority of the captain far too soon.)

ALTITUDE The height expressed in units of distance above a reference plane, usually above mean sea level or ground level.

ATTENTION The ability of an individual human to concentrate on one or more tasks.

AUTOMATION The process by which machines (usually computer-controlled in aircraft) accomplish the tasks normally performed by humans.

AROUSAL (CONCEPTS OF) Related to stress. A person's state of arousal is a good way of demonstrating an individual's preparedness for a difficult task. Experts believe that arousal and performance are related by an inverted V-shaped curve (known as the Yerkes-Dodson curve). Deep sleep is at one end, extreme panic the other. Both result in poor performance. Optimum arousal is the mid-point between the two.

BLIND SPOT A small area on the retina of the eye in which no vision is possible due to the attachment of the optic nerve.

CLOSED-LOOP SYSTEM A system which the operator has the ability to control once it is in motion, based on the continuous feedback of information.

CONCEPT MAP A graphic depiction of the relationships between ideas, information or concepts. Each idea (or concept) has a number of associated ideas. Each one can be put within a square or circle, then interlinked as required to provide an overall map.

COCKPIT RESOURCE MANAGEMENT Which has also been known as Flight Deck Management, Practical Cockpit Management, and now Crew Resource Management to conform to international regulatory agreement. Company-Crew Resource Management has recently been given some airing in official CRM discussions, but this takes in a whole new range of issues, raising controversy among training experts about how far CRM training should go outside the cockpit environment.) Therefore the basic CRM concept is the process of managing all resources in and out of the cockpit, to promote safe flying operations whatever they may be. These resources not only include the human element, but also mechanical, computer and other supporting systems. It is an extension of pilot judgement to the multi-person flightcrew, although the principles of CRM can be equally well applied to single-pilot situations. The primary focus of CRM is on communication, both within the cockpit crew and with those outside such as ATC, company and traffic. Communication is the most critical factor in cockpit management, because it is the means by which effective management is carried out.

COMPUTER-BASED TRAINING (CBT) Meaning the use of a computer – usually a micro-computer – for teaching knowledge and skills. This is also known as Computer-Based Education (CBE), Computer-Based Instruction (CBI), and Computer-Assisted Instruction (CAI).

COMPLACENCY When activities become routine, as most flights usually are, it is easy for flight crews to relax and not put as much effort into their performance. Automation has the potential of lulling pilots into the expectation that all flights will be routine, because so much of the work is done by the systems. Pilots must always guard against complacency.

CONTROLLED AIRSPACE Airspace designated as a control zone, airport radar service area, continental control area or positive control area, within which some or all of the aircraft may be subject to air traffic control.

DECISIVENESS Leaders view decisiveness as an essential binding influence for unity of action. Followers will usually excuse almost any stupidity, indiscretion, or ill-conceived action, but they will not accept excessive timidity.

DECISION The seventh step of the judgement process. At this point the pilot has made up his mind what to do, and is now ready to act. This step requires leadership skills.

DISORIENTATION In essence, the *sense* of not being orientated.

DECIDE TECHNIQUE This technique was developed to improve mental organisation and agility, so that you can prevent overlooking important facts. When a pilot is faced with any decision involving uncertainty, the DECIDE mnemonic will help you to remember the essential order:

Detect: The fact that a change has occurred which requires attention.

Estimate: What significance this has on the flight.

Choose: A safe method to ensure a satisfactory outcome to the flight.

Identify: Realistic actions while evaluating the risks and carrying out the necessary changes (solutions).

Do: Carry out the best option.

Evaluate: The effect of the actions taken on the flight progress.

Using this technique in the real world of flight operations, you need to be a vigilant monitor of all factors that could influence change during the flight. When this occurs, use the DECIDE process. Start with decisions that have an element of uncertainty such as meteorological forecasts, fuel calculations and navigation uncertainties. Frequent use will bring familiarity and will help you in all your flight decisions.

EXPECTANCY In every situation in which you become involved, whether this is on the ground or in the air, you develop an awareness of the predictable elements of the situation. From this awareness you learn to expect certain things to happen.

ENVIRONMENT Means influences other than the aircraft, for example the weather and its associated factors, take-off and landing distances available, the terrain being overflown, etc.

FANS The Future Air Navigation System concept. It marks the emergence of the next generation of air traffic management systems that will ultimately replace current voice-based systems. Part of FANS is the replacement of all routine communications by computer data links, of which ACARS (Aircraft Communications Addressing and Reporting System) is one. ACARS uses a computer terminal in the aircraft communicating by digital data bursts over a VHF radio link to a network of ground stations.

FIXATION Is the condition that occurs when you focus intently on one object to the exclusion of everything else. It is not strictly a visual condition, but is closely related to attention. However, it occurs more often when the visual system is involved.

FINAL APPROACH The flight path of a landing aircraft, flying in the direction of landing, which is along the extended runway centreline straight in to the runway, or from the base leg position on the airfield circuit to then line up with the runway.

GLASS COCKPIT A cockpit in which most of the instruments are electronically displayed on a computer monitor (Cathode Ray Tube Display – CRT).

GROUND PROXIMITY WARNING SYSTEM (GPWS) An alarm in the cockpit which indicates when the aircraft is too close to the ground.

HUMAN FACTORS The study of how people interact with their environments. In the case of general aviation, it is the study of how pilot performance is influenced by such issues as design of cockpits, functions of the organs of the body, effects of emotions, and interaction and communication with other personnel within the aviation community, i.e. flightcrew colleagues, ground operations and traffic staff, meteorological forecasters and assistants, plus air traffic control.

HYPERVENTILATION Excessive ventilation of the lungs caused by very rapid and deep breathing, which results in an excessive loss of carbon dioxide from the body.

HYPOXIA The effects on the human body of an insufficient supply of oxygen; can be hypoxic, anaemic, stagnant or histotoxic in nature.

ILLUSION The incorrect interpretation of spoken, aural or visual information.

INCIDENT An occurrence other than an accident associated with the operation of an aircraft, which affects or could affect the safety of operations.

INQUIRY Or information-seeking, is the first aspect of communication. It represents the start point in the process of making effective decisions. Good decisions are based on good information. On the flight deck, inquiry consists of gathering information from the visual scan and from questioning other crew members, or outside sources, such as air traffic control. It also means asking for clarification when the information is not clearly understood, checking instruments, radios, charts and visually scanning for aircraft outside the cockpit.

INVULNERABILITY This particular attitude is found in people who believe that accidents always happen to others, not to them. The usual comment is, 'It won't happen to me!' This is a very dangerous trait in pilots, and can easily lead to the development of dangerous situations.

INSTRUMENT FLIGHT RULES (IFR) Rules which govern the procedure for conducting flight in instrument weather conditions. When weather conditions are below the minimums prescribed for VFR, only instrument-rated pilots may fly in accordance with IFR.

INSTRUMENT METEOROLOGICAL CONDITIONS Weather conditions requiring flight under IFR.

INTERACTIVE VIDEO A subset of CBT, using both video and computer-generated images for training. It is an essential element in CRM and LOFT training.

INTERFERENCE The condition when one source of information interferes with an individual's ability to process another.

INTERNATIONAL CIVIL AVIATION ORGANISATION (ICAO) Part of the United Nations. It is the international body which co-ordinates and advises on international regulation of civil aviation for member states.

JUDGEMENT Perceptual judgement is the ability to make visual decisions, such as height above the ground when landing; cognitive judgement is the process of making intellectual decisions.

MAXIMUM WORKLOAD CAPACITY Each pilot has a maximum workload capacity which is a function of many factors. This includes experience, proficiency level, specific training (on type, or types, being flown), motivation, emotional health and inherent skill. Maximum pilot capacity can be degraded by any number or combination of factors, e.g. fatigue, family and marital problems, job-related stress, illness, lack of training, lack of proficiency, and any other cause which has an effect on individual piloting skills or reduces situational awareness. A pilot's maximum workload capacity can vary for any given flight. This will be based on any combination of degrading factors specific to the pilot's lifestyle at a particular time. Therefore that capacity will change from day to day, from flight to flight and even during a flight itself.

MEMORY (SHORT-TERM) Is the memory you have of events and information received in the very recent past, which is usually no more than half a minute. It has a small capacity and a high rate of decay.

MEMORY (LONG-TERM) This is considered permanent storage. Information that is rehearsed, meaning practised, or is of considerable importance, may be suitably translated and transferred into permanent storage in long-term memory. The total mental capacity is much greater and the decay rate is slower.

MOTIVATION A force coming from within the brain that causes a person to act or behave in certain ways. It is usually considered a positive force, because it causes that person to act or move forward as opposed to remaining stagnant. Motivation shows itself either in intensity or in direction.

MAN-MACHINE SYSTEM A collection of components some of which are machines, at least one of which is human, that technically co-operate and work together to accomplish specific tasks.

MILLIBAR A unit of atmospheric pressure equal to a force of 1,000 dynes per square centimetre.

NATIONAL TRANSPORTATION SAFETY BOARD (NTSB) The organisation with the authority to oversee the safety of the United States Transportation Systems. It undertakes investigations of aircraft accidents. In keeping with an internationally recognised expert image like the FBI, the NTSB has been called upon to help with air accident investigations in foreign countries at their request, when some particular specialist expertise has been required.

OPEN-LOOP SYSTEM A system in which the operator has no control once it is in motion.

ORIENTATION This relates to knowing which way is up, and is very critical in flying because the senses find it more difficult to tell what is happening in relationship to the earth's surface. It is impossible to maintain orientation when flying by only using the body's sensory organs alone, unless you can see the horizon.

PILOT ERROR An action or decision of the pilot that if not caught and corrected could contribute to the occurrence of an accident or incident. We can include in this inaction by the pilot, or indecision, as both can be contributory factors in pilot error.

PILOT SAFETY Pilots need aircraft in order to fly, but to fly safely pilots must have the ability not only to control their aircraft and equipment, but also to control themselves and their thought processes. Without this the pilot becomes the most vulnerable 'flight system' in the aircraft.

PILOT-IN-COMMAND The pilot responsible for the operation and safety of an aircraft and the passengers carried in it. This pilot has legal accreditation in international law.

PILOT JUDGEMENT The mental process that a pilot uses in making decisions.

POOR JUDGEMENT CHAIN A series of judgement errors.

PSYCHOMOTOR SKILL A skill that needs a combination of perceptual, cognitive and motor skills.

RUNWAY THRESHOLD The beginning of the landing area of the runway. The actual threshold is usually marked by reasonably broad parallel white lines, so it will be clearly visible to pilots in all weather conditions and at night.

RISK MANAGEMENT Involves good judgement and decision-making, which is all about the way we think, or do not think, as the case may be

RISK ANALYSIS This is the fifth step of the judgement process. During this stage the pilot analyses the risk(s) involved in taking each of the identified alternatives. These may be available either to solve or avoid a problem, and require mental creativity and knowledge.

RESIGNATION People who feel they have no control over their fate tend to acquire this attitude. The stock phrase, 'What's the use, I can't do anything about it?', is liable to be used. They are even more likely to go along with unreasonable requests just to be thought of as 'the nice guy'. It is not likely that they will be respected because of this attitude.

SITUATIONAL AWARENESS A constant and accurate perception of the factors and conditions which affect the aircraft and flightcrew. In other words it is knowing what is going on around you, therefore the higher your state of situational awareness the lower the risk.

STANDARD ATMOSPHERE A hypothetical atmosphere based on averages in which the surface temperature is 15°C (59°F), with a surface pressure of 1,013.2 millibars (29.92 inches Hg) at sea level. The temperature lapse rate is approximately 2 deg. C per 1,000 feet.

STRESSOR Something that causes stress.

STRESS The body's response to demands placed on it. PHYSICAL: The physical response to stressors such as heat, noise and vibration. PHYSIOLOGICAL: The response to stressors such as fatigue, lack of sleep and improper diet. EMOTIONAL: The body's response to emotional or social stressors. This includes marital problems, peer pressure, fear, anger and euphoria. The improper use of medication or drugs can lead to considerable emotional stress.

STRUCTURE PRACTICE Means the emphasis on developing the pilot's mental skills. After problem-solving, exercising good judgement and improving performance comes the physical or psychomotor skills of flying and controlling the aircraft. In point of fact, safety in flying is actually dependent more on good thinking (analysing) and subsequent processing skills than it is on how well the pilot manipulates the controls.

TYPE-A PERSON People have behaviour patterns that are generally seen as a major cause of coronary heart disease. The Type-A personality frequently appears on the aviation scene. They are characterised by a competitive, aggressive, achievement-orientated, time-dominated orientation to life. Type-A pilots are seldom aware of their behaviour, or that it is detrimental to their health, and in many instances inter-personal as well as professional relationships. Unfortunately they seem to end up in management pilot or managerial positions, and their behaviour frequently creates problems for people around them who have more stable personalities.

TASK LOADING The actual cockpit workload required for the safe performance of any phase of flight. There is always a nominal pilot task loading for each phase of flight. However, due to a variety of operational influences task loading can increase gradually or suddenly. The pilot must have the ability to deal with this to ensure the successful completion of the flight. The causes of increased task loading include:

- abnormal or emergency situations
- aircraft system problems
- adverse weather

- high density of air traffic leading to in-flight delays
- company pressures, including schedule changes

THEORY OF THE SITUATION What you assume to be true, based on your perception of the facts you have available at any point in time.

THEORY IN PRACTICE The set of skills, knowledge and experience you call upon, according to your theory of the situation.

TRACK The actual path of an aircraft over the ground.

VESTIBULAR SYSTEM The system of the inner ear that provides information concerning the body's orientation.

VISUAL FLIGHT RULES (VFR) Rules which govern the procedures for conducting flight in visual conditions. The term VFR is also used to indicate weather conditions which comply with specified VFR requirements.

WORKLOAD PHYSICAL: The amount of simultaneous physical activity performed by a human. MENTAL: The amount of simultaneous mental activity performed by a human.

Index